Praise for *Yoga Cocaine*

"We all lose our way at some time in our lives, and if lucky, we awaken, our hearts soften and we manage to find our way home again. A raw, compelling, artfully crafted novel, *Yoga Cocaine* takes us on a deep dive into the shadowy world of addiction. This novel powerfully illuminates what's available to us when we commit ourselves to the redemptive path of recovery. Even if you've never struggled with addiction, you will be shaken, moved and inspired."

Kezia Renée Lechner, author of
Close to the Bone: An Uncommon Love Story

"*Yoga Cocaine* is a heart wrenching story of a woman failing at what seems like an impossible mission: getting sober. Yet, she doesn't give up, instead finding ways to keep trying and learning how to be a better version of herself, with help and a lot of yoga. Its intense, matter-of-fact voice draws us into Jessica's world, walking us through her journey in a way that helps us to see into the mind of an addict and understand how long and hard a journey it really is."

Selina J. Eckert, author of *This Cursed Flame*

"Jessica's experiences could put any fraternity guy to shame, yet you feel for her and root for her, despite her nonexistent moral compass. Through yoga, and some serious diversions, she undergoes a powerful, poignant transformation. *Yoga Cocaine* is an emotional rollercoaster ride of despair and recovery. It's a must read for anyone who's ever dealt with addiction or loves yoga."

Heidi Doheny Jay, author of *Confessions of 400 Men*

"For anyone who has known addiction and sobriety—or wondered about it—*Yoga Cocaine* is a powerful, painful, hopeful, inspiring and addicting story that you won't be able to put down. Pick it up now and dive in."

Lisa Kohn, author of
To the Moon and Back: A Childhood Under the Influence

"*Yoga Cocaine* combines 12-Step Recovery with mindfulness techniques—always a perfect marriage. Highly relatable and clearly written, it makes a helpful contribution to recovery literature. This work embraces all the messiness and magic of the path to enlightenment. Namaste, Daralyse Lyons. Thank you for your beautifully imperfect perfection."

Richard A. Singer Jr., author of
101 Tips for Recovery from Addiction

"For most of her life, Jessica has been hurting and knows the most reliable way to escape her demons is through drugs, alcohol, sex and... yoga. In the moving *Yoga Cocaine*, Daralyse Lyons plunges her reader into the rocky world of addiction and recovery, where honesty and friendship (and a decent frog pose) carve the pathway toward hope."

Sarahlyn Bruck, author of *Designer You*

"An edgy, gritty narrative about the challenges of addiction and the healing power of yoga, with guidance for everyone on how to incorporate yoga practice to aspire to our better selves."

Jacqui Lipton, author and literary agent

Yoga Cocaine

By Daralyse Lyons

Modern History Press
Ann Arbor, MI

Library of Congress Cataloging-in-Publication Data

Names: Lyons, Daralyse, author.
Title: Yoga cocaine / by Daralyse Lyons.
Description: First edition. | Ann Arbor, MI : Modern History Press, [2019] | Summary: "Jessica has multiple addiction issues, including cocaine, marijuana, and alcohol. After her latest suicide attempt, she makes a wholehearted leap into an Alcoholics Anonymous program. However, her recovery will be long, lonely, and extremely challenging... and with a little help from yoga, she just might get clean and find a healthy relationship"-- Provided by publisher.
Identifiers: LCCN 2019042165 (print) | LCCN 2019042166 (ebook) | ISBN 9781615994847 (trade paperback) | ISBN 9781615994854 (hardcover) | ISBN
9781615994861 (kindle edition) | ISBN 9781615994861 (epub)
Classification: LCC PS3612.Y5744 Y64 2019 (print) | LCC PS3612.Y5744 (ebook) | DDC 813/.6--dc23
LC record available at https://lccn.loc.gov/2019042165
LC ebook record available at https://lccn.loc.gov/2019042166

Published by
Modern History Press
5145 Pontiac Trail
Ann Arbor, MI 48105

Tollfree 888-761-6268
FAX 734-663-6861

www.ModernHistoryPress.com
info@ModernHIstoryPress.com

Distributed by Ingram (USA/CAN/AU), Bertram's Books (UK/EU)

The Twelve Steps of Cocaine Anonymous

1. We admitted we were powerless over cocaine and all other mind-altering substances—that our lives had become unmanageable.
2. Came to believe that a power greater than ourselves could restore us to sanity.
3. Made a decision to turn our will and our lives over to the care of God *as we understood Him.*
4. Made a searching and fearless moral inventory of ourselves.
5. Admitted to God, to ourselves, and to another human being the exact nature of our wrongs.
6. Were entirely ready to have God remove all these defects of character.
7. Humbly asked Him to remove our shortcomings.
8. Made a list of all persons we had harmed, and became willing to make amends to them all.
9. Made direct amends to such people wherever possible, except when to do so would injure them or others.
10. Continued to take personal inventory, and when we were wrong, promptly admitted it.
11. Sought through prayer and meditation to improve our conscious contact with God *as we understood Him*, praying only for knowledge of His will for us and the power to carry that out.
12. Having had a spiritual awakening as the result of these steps, we tried to carry this message to other addicts, and to practice these principles in all our affairs.

Part I

Pose

Child's Pose (Balasana)

Kneel on your yoga mat, touching your big toes together beneath you. Separate your knees a hip's width apart and lower your buttocks down onto your heels. Relax your torso completely as you fold forward, over your thighs. Allow the gentle curvature of your spine to dictate the position of your arms, which can rest alongside your body or stretch out in front of you.

Prayer

Serenity Prayer

God, grant me the serenity to accept the things I cannot change, courage to change the things I can, and the wisdom to know the difference.

Promise

"Nearly all have recovered. They have solved the drink problem." (*Alcoholics Anonymous Big Book*, p. 17)

Step One:

We admitted we were powerless over cocaine—that our lives had become unmanageable. (Easy Pose)

1

I'm not exactly Zen. Sure, I do yoga. I chant and bow a reverent Namaste to Sati, my beautiful, waif-like yoga teacher, but last night I did a line of coke off the backseat of a toilet and this morning I woke up awash in my own vomit. So, no Zen zone for me.

The worst part of being hung-over in yoga is that, before last night, I had a week sober. Still, I'm here. I've dragged myself to Sati's class on a crisp March Friday morning, unrolled my wilted mat, and plastered on my emptiest, most vacant, expression.

"Stand in Tadasana." Sati is a fucking fruitarian. She reeks of patchouli.

As I stand at the top of my mat, my body swaying, in spite of my brain's instructions for it to stay still, I don't feel sturdy, like a mountain. I feel like quicksand—a bottomless pit of need.

"Be the pose," my teacher says. "Embody your most enlightened self."

Enlightenment, my ass. She can keep her patchouli and her fruitarianism. I'm here to sweat out toxins, so I can stop feeling like an animal carcass that's been decomposing in the noonday sun. I breathe. My mind drifts back to last night in a bar in Center City—the straw, the white confectioner's sugar (as sweet and addictive as candy), the heady rush. *That* was Nirvana. This is a room full of middle-aged white women with the bodies of twenty-year-old girls.

I'm thirty-two, too old to be doing coke, too young to stop.

Shit. Everyone else has stretched their arms toward the sky and I'm still standing at the top of my mat. I reach up too late, fold forward several seconds after my Sun Saluting peers. I don't catch up 'til Chaturanga.

"Lower your body into a pushup."

That reminds me... I left my push up bra in the backseat of some stranger's car last night. I didn't have sex with him. He wanted to. I did too. Until I puked.

I got out of the car to clean myself in the bar's gender-neutral bathroom, and, when I returned, the guy had disappeared, taking my bra with him.

"Downward Dog," Sati says. "Or, if your body, not your mind, has a desire to flow, take a vinyasa."

I don't flow.

She materializes behind me and adjusts my hips. "Nice form, Jessica."

I catch another whiff of campfire, mint and charcoal and fight the impulse to hurl. It was a bad idea to come to this power-yoga-masquerading-as-Mt.-Airy-crunchy-granola class. I should've stayed in bed and slept through the hangover, and the regret.

The woman in front of me is wearing oversized underwear. It bunches over the top of her spandex. I try not to giggle, but laughter leaks out of me. Like sweat.

I hope my sweat doesn't smell like beer.

One time, I went to a hot yoga class the day after a bender and flooded the room with the noxious scent of skunk piss, with the accompanying undercurrent of rubbing alcohol. Luckily, everyone there was too "enlightened" to confront me.

I'm such an addict. But, no matter how many times I fail, I keep going to meetings and coming to yoga because my sponsor assures me that, if I do, at some point, my life will amount to more than a series of disappointments.

"Utkatasana," Sati says. "Padangusthasana."

I'm craving euphoria. It doesn't come. Yoga is a poor substitute for cocaine.

2

"I'm not going out with you, Jimmy." I glower across the counter.

He looks back at me. Big brown eyes, a pockmarked face, a slightly crooked smile. I wish he'd see that I'm too good for him and stop asking me out. Alright, maybe not the me I am now—this me is working for $7.25 an hour at a lame Mt. Airy coffee shop—but the me I'm going to be. After I quit.

I hand Jimmy his cappuccino. I've been working at the Free Café for six months now (five months past when I thought I'd get my life together). Jimmy works down the street at his parents' deli. Like I'd ever date some minimum-wage sandwich-pusher. The only reason I'm living in coffee hell is because I was fired from my last three legit jobs. Apparently, it's frowned upon to get high on company time, make out with coworkers, and steal money out of petty cash.

My not-so-secret admirer looks as forlorn as a puppy that's been turned away, treat-less, after begging for scraps. "Jessica, I'm a nice guy who wants to take you out on a date. You could do worse."

"For sure," I reply. "That's what I'm waiting for—worse."

I'm only half kidding. I have a thing for assholes. Or, rather, asshole's things have a thing for me. Sober or shitfaced, I walk into any room and dysfunction finds me. That's part of the reason I haven't been to an AA meeting in a couple weeks. The last time I went, I met Garrett. He had four days sober. I had four minutes. We fucked in the bathroom.

Before AA, I had a few sessions with a therapist because I knew something was wrong and didn't know how to fix it. After several appointments, some of which I arrived to mildly intoxicated, or missed altogether, she told me I was "unpredictable" and "lacked emotional integrity."

Predictably, I fired her. Well, actually, since I lacked the integrity to tell her, I stopped showing up.

Now, I have April—my infinitely patient sponsor.

A few weeks ago, I heard this guy say in a meeting that, every time he sees his golden retriever, he thinks about how the word *dog* is *God* spelled backward, and how knowing that draws him closer to his Higher Power. The last dog I had, I sold to a neighbor kid for fifty bucks for drug money. April behaves kind of like a dog. She's always happy to see me, and, every time I call, she comes. I called her this morning, which is why, when I look up from wiping down the counter, she's walking through the door.

Jimmy slinks out, leaving my sponsor and me alone. Now, she's free to lecture without worrying about breaking either of our anonymity.

"Jess." April's tone is parental. "You have to call *before* you pick up. Not after."

April does yoga too. She got me into it.

"Why do you always call *after*?"

I don't answer her question. We both know why I don't call before getting high. I don't want to be talked out of it.

"You can choose your rock bottom, you know. You don't have to lose everything."

What else is there to lose? Last year, at Thanksgiving, my mom and stepdad disowned me for getting drunk and smoking dope. Well, not really. They disowned me because, in a fit of paranoia, I threw the turkey out the window, then dove under the table and screamed "It's gonna explode!" I thought the poultry was a bomb.

I wasn't wrong about an explosion. My stepdad blew up.

He screamed at me so loud the table shook. When I finally crawled out, Mom was crying and my sister—who is younger than I am, but more mature than I'll ever be—whipped my car keys at my face and told me to get out.

Seeing Chloe lose her composure almost made it worth it. Almost.

"Fuck you!" I shrieked as I stumbled out the door. "I don't need any of you!"

My triumph was short-lived. I tripped on the front stoop, fell headfirst into a rosebush, and puked onto the grass.

The Chinese food delivery man who arrived half an hour later with a roast duck—Mom's last-minute solution to the turkey predicament—saved me. Ping (that was his name) helped me up, walked me to my car, and gave me a bottle of water.

I'd have thanked him, but I was too fixated on my memories of the children's book Mom and Dad used to read out-loud to Chloe and me. "You have the name of a duck, and you're delivering duck," I said, over and over, between fits of giggles.

"You no dribe 'til you no drunk," the delivery guy cautioned.

"Duck!" I clutched my aching abdomen. Between the belly laughs and the puking, it had gotten quite the workout.

"I no time this." Ping wagged a disapproving finger in my face.

I leaned my dizzy head against the steering wheel.

A horn blast. Dwight standing at the door.

"I back, one minute."

Ping finished his delivery, checked on me one last time, then left. "You no dribe," he reiterated. "You danj'ous lady, ve'y drunk."

I spent the next few hours sobering up in Mom and Dwight's driveway before heading home to sleep the rest of the holiday away.

"Jess...?"

The counter is now sparkling. I've been ceaselessly scrubbing the same spot.

My sponsor's expression is equal-parts pity and love. All she wants is for me to be sober. I bite my lower lip to keep my eyes from betraying me. No way will I allow myself to cry. Just as I'm about to reply, my coworker, Tina, comes in to start her shift.

"Hey, you're like Jess' friend, right?"

Tina is a shy, smiley girl who wears pigtails and uses the word *like* as a verb, noun and adjective. Her nails are pumpkin orange today, despite it being nowhere near Halloween.

"I should get back to work."

April lowers her voice so my Valley Girl coworker won't overhear. "Want to go to a meeting after your shift?"

Not really, I think, but what comes out of my mouth is "Can we go to a women's meeting?"

I don't want to risk running into Garrett.

I haven't told April about Garrett. I'm not looking to get a reputation. I already *have* a reputation. I'm looking to undo it.

3

When my shift ends, I hurry home to shower, eat, stare at my kitchen wall, and try not to obsess about how pissed I am with myself that, once again, I forfeited my sobriety or that, in spite of my self-recrimination, I'm still longing to get high. I wait until the last possible second before heading out the door.

At 6:59, I walk into the Church of the Nazarene and slide into the empty chair beside my sponsor. I've calculated my arrival like I calculate so many things in life. 6:59 is the perfect time to get to a seven o'clock meeting. This way, I don't have to make conversation, which I'd have to do if I were early, and I don't draw attention to myself by being late.

The only thing I can't seem to calculate is what will happen if I take a drink, or succumb to an urge to use. Every time I pick up, I think, *This time will be different. This time will be worth it.*

April squeezes my knee.

The Chestnut Hill Friday Night Women's Meeting used to be her home group back when she was single and lived seventeen miles away, in South Philadelphia, but drove here every week to escape the possible shame of someone from her neighborhood recognizing her.

I don't care about that. I live three miles down the road in Mt. Airy and I'm pretty sure everyone in my neighborhood knows I'm an addict. I just don't want them to know what a failure I am at trying to quit.

The meeting leader reads the traditions. When she gets to "The only requirement for AA membership is the desire to stop drinking," it's all I can do to keep myself from running out. As much as I want to want to stop—and to be rid of the consequences—the truth is, I don't. In fact, I'd give anything for an ice cold beer right now.

"The floor is now for sharing." I raise my hand at the same time as some perky, pink-cloud divorcee. The meeting leader calls on her.

"Hi. I'm Amber, and I'm an alcoholic. I'm so *grateful* right now, because…"

What follows is a stream of verbal diarrhea about kids and playdates and feeling present and living life on life's terms and how even her ex-husband has come to respect her. Bo-ring. The next sharer is much better. She talks about how life still blows, but how it blows less now that she's not doing blow. Her irreverence makes me laugh, which is good because I have trouble concentrating—even here, amidst who are supposed to be "my people."

I wish I had the capacity to be mindful off the mat, but, most of the time, I can't even be mindful on it. Still, I do my best to tune in. These women seem to have figured out how to enjoy life enough not to want to go through it numb. My only hope is to learn from their experiences.

Next to me, my sponsor's right hand rises while her left remains neatly in her lap, its pinky-adjacent finger adorned with the spectacular platinum and diamond noose of commitment.

April met and married Howie after she got sober. He only knows her as dependable.

"Hi, I'm April and I'm and addict and alcoholic."

"Hi, April."

"I'm grateful to be here tonight—grateful to be sober, period. A decade and a half ago, I was having sex with men for crack and about to be evicted from yet another apartment. Now, I've got almost fifteen years sober."

The women clap and cheer, lavishing their approval on someone who no longer needs it because she has the confidence that comes from nearly 5,475 accumulated drink-less, drugless days.

"My life today isn't what I'd ever have imagined. The highs aren't as high, but they're sustainable. And, as for the lows, my worst day sober is a million times better than my best day using."

When it's my turn to share, I stumble through my introduction. "I'm Jess-Jesse-Jessica. I'm an alcoholic and an addict."

The room erupts in a chorus of "Hi Jessica!"s

I don't know why they're so chipper. It's not like I've got anything profound to say. Everyone in this church basement has more abstinence, and more wisdom, than I ever will.

"I'm in a fucked up place," I admit. "I'll get a few days, or a week. Then, I find myself picking up again. I want to have hit bottom. I mean, I've lost my family, friends, jobs, money, and self-respect, and, most days, I wake up and wish I hadn't, but, even though I hate the person drugs and alcohol have turned me into, I can't tell you I won't drink tomorrow."

Several heads nod. A few of the old-timers murmur that I should "keep coming back."

"Sorry to be a downer," I tell the room. "Thanks for letting me share."

And then it happens. That familiar sensation washes over me. That sensation I get during every AA meeting, and at the end of every yoga class.

It feels like Shavasana. It feels like home.

4

After the meeting, April walks me to my car.

My keys jangle in my shaky grasp.

"Promise you'll go home?" It's part question, part command.

Despite the momentary reprieve, my thoughts have turned to liquor. I don't want to get *drunk*, but *one* drink wouldn't hurt. I could get a martini. Or a piña colada. Something girly with hardly any alcohol.

The first person to give me alcohol was my stepdad. Initially, I didn't like the taste. But I liked sharing a secret.

Don't tell your mother.

"Jess?"

I study the scuff marks on the insoles of my boots. When did those get there?

"Jess...?"

For once, I win the fight against my inner addict and tell April the truth. "I can't make that promise."

She reaches out her hand, palm up, the underbelly of her wedding and engagement shackles gleaming in the darkness. I give her my keys then follow her to her BMW. Climb into the passenger seat. Put on my seatbelt. It's a familiar routine. April will drive us the twenty-seven traffic-free minutes to her stately Colonial on the Main Line in Wayne, just 3.9 miles away from where I grew up—also on the Main Line, in Bryn Mawr, where Mom and Dwight still live in the container of my memories. Tonight, I'll sleep on April's couch. In the morning, I'll eat breakfast with her husband and their smiling six and eight-year-old daughters and pretend not to be wigged out by their cookie-cutter suburban lives.

April makes perfect pancakes and her girls refer to me as "Aunt Jess" and ask to braid my hair and wonder out loud why I don't have a husband.

"You're pretty and nice," they tell me. "You should at least have a boyfriend."

I was ten when my stepdad offered me my first beer. We sipped in tandem while watching the Eagles play the 49ers. When the Eagles won, Dwight called me his "lucky charm."

In the morning, on his way to work, Howie will drive me back to this church parking lot and I'll have amassed exactly twenty-four hours.

“Thanks.”

My real dad died when I was five and Chloe was a few weeks shy of two. He had a streak of white in his hair, in the front, and, after he was gone, I used to watch Maxwell Sheffield in *The Nanny* and pretend he was my dad. Once, hours into a *Nanny* marathon, Mom told me to turn off the TV and I dissolved into a sobbing pile on the floor. It took her forever to get me to explain why I was so upset.

“I can’t turn Daddy off!” I finally wailed, after an hour’s worth of coaxing.

But Daddy hadn’t had an English accent or three blazer-wearing offspring. Just messy, unhinged me, my perfect baby sister, and a wife who was very much alive.

“Don’t thank me.” April hits the button on her key fob, unlocking the doors. “Just get sober, then pass on the miracle to another fucked-up addict.”

“Like me.” I climb in and slam the door.

She slides into the driver’s seat and gently closes hers. “Like us.”

≠ 5 ≠

I meet Oliver at the Saturday Serenity Meeting on the first Saturday in April. Looking at him, I can't help but think of sailing regattas and country clubs. But, to hear him tell it, before he got sober, he was more Motley Crew than J. Crew. He raises his hand and, when the meeting leader calls on him, talks about how he has nearly eleven months sober and how, when he'd first dragged himself through the doors of AA, he'd been an unwashed, angry mess.

"It didn't matter though. In AA, the uglier you are, the more love you get."

Everyone laughs. He's right. Twelve-Step fellowships are a conglomerate of misfits.

After eleven months of sobriety, Oliver is no longer disheveled. On this crisp, spring night, he's wearing a button-down polo shirt, Ralph Lauren khakis, and a friggin' cardigan. He's way too straight-laced to ever be my type, but his share about redemption struck a chord with me. More than anything, I want to be saved—from myself.

After the meeting, Oliver approaches. "How are you?"

"Fine. You?"

"Good."

I don't say anything.

"I haven't seen you at this meeting before."

He's cute—in an unremarkable, boy-next-door kind of way. "I haven't been to this meeting before."

"So, how long have you been sober?"

"Long enough." Eight days. "Congratulations on your eleven months."

"Thanks. Want to help me celebrate?"

I lean in, the way I would if I were at a bar, trying to entice a stranger into buying me a drink, and whisper low, so only he can hear me. "What do you have in mind?"

"You're so fucking hot!"

I'm not sure who's more surprised by the outburst—me, Oliver, or the old guy at the coffee pot who snarls his disapproval.

Oliver claps a hand over his mouth and turns a deep shade of burgundy. The old guy mutters something about AA not being a pick-up joint and how, back in his day, thirteenth-steppers got what was coming to them. I bite my bottom lip to keep from laughing.

"I can't believe I said that." Oliver's voice is a whisper now. "You seem like a great girl. I just don't know if I'm ready for a relationship. You *are* sexy though. During the meeting, I couldn't stop looking at you and fantasizing about–"

I cut him off. "What makes you think I want a relationship?"

"Um... Well... I... Um... We..."

"You're pretty hot yourself." I hand Motley Crew Makeover ten digits, scribbled on a scrap of paper. Halfway through the meeting, I pre-wrote my number just in case. "Text me. We'll see where it goes."

An hour later, I'm on the couch—a Bioré Pore Strip on my nose—watching Mr. Belvedere on ANT when my cellphone pings.

I just thought about you.

Yeah? What were you doing?

Jerking off.

To keep it interesting, I wait ten minutes before replying.

It's easy to be bold via text.

Oliver tells me he wants to fuck me. I tell him I want to lick him—flaccid and erect. We pick a date. Establish a time.

Do you want to meet for dinner or something? he wants to know.

No relationship, I remind him. I'm not interested in making small talk, just in fucking.

And in forgetting I should write. Sex is a mode of escape for me. It fills the empty spaces.

For a while, my stepdad and I had a good thing going. He'd give me money for clothes and alcohol to bring with me to parties and cover for me with Mom when I stayed out past curfew. After all, the boys my age were hopeless. They never knew what to do with their lips and tongues and hands. Not like Dwight.

Before I even have a chance to knock, Oliver opens his big, wooden townhouse door. I fight the urge to laugh. Is he really wearing an olive green sweater vest?

Hard to reconcile this Mr. Rogers look-alike with the sex-obsessed pervert who's been sending me *What're you wearing?* texts.

"Do you want a tour?"

"Not really."

"Want to watch TV?"

I shake my head.

"Can I get you something to drink? Orangina...? Cream Soda...? Fanta...? Perrier...?"

I interrupt him before he can rattle off any more beverage offerings. "I'm not here to get a tour of your place or make conversation. I'm here to fuck."

I hadn't realized a jaw could come so unhinged without serious, surgical intervention. It takes Oliver a full thirty seconds to collect himself. When he does, he pulls me close and presses his lips to mine. I open my mouth, inviting him deeper. As our tongues tangle, I can feel his expanse of well-muscled chest beneath his ridiculous sweater.

We stumble awkwardly up the stairs to his bedroom, tripping through what should be an easy ascension because neither of us wants to stop kissing long enough to look where we're going. When we reach his bed, I push him down and let my lips descend, tracing Oliver's midline with my tongue, until I arrive at the center of his sex. Then, I take him into my mouth and feel the pleasure-wave that sweeps through his body, threatening to pull him under.

I am a drug, powerful and thrilling.

"Oh, God!"

Why do people call out to God during sex? If there is a God, which I'm not sure there is, do we really want to call His attention to the fact that we're fucking? And, if there isn't, then isn't calling out "God" the equivalent of being in bed with one guy and accidentally screaming someone else's name?

"Hold on." Oliver pulls me up by the shoulders, reaches into his bedside table, and takes out a condom.

I slip out of my underwear and unhook my bra. It's been a while since I've had bedroom sex. The last few times have been in backseats or bathrooms. Or in alleys, like feral cats. But here Oliver and I are, two virtual strangers, naked and sober.

He rolls on. Or tries to. The condom won't adhere to his shaft.

He smiles at me, mildly abashed. I smile back. His penis pulsates, keeping rhythm with his heartbeat, as he pulls out a second condom and...

Oops. It slips off too.

His smile falters. "What the hell?"

I want to tell Oliver that he needs to dry off his junk, so the rubber has something to cling to, but advising a guy about prophylactic application is like trying to give him driving directions, so I sit, unmoving, on the edge of the bed and wait for him to figure out what I already know.

Another condom—the last one—this time snatched furiously from the same bedside drawer. Another failed attempt. The three, useless condoms form a pile of wet rubber on Oliver's bedroom floor.

"It doesn't matter," I tell him.

And it doesn't. Not to me. Not in this moment anyway.

I take Oliver into my mouth again and lick, suck, kiss, and caress until he forgets about the wet, wilted schlong shields and writhes in ecstasy, overpowered by desire. I climb on. Straddle him. Gyrate—slowly at first, then faster.

Beneath me, Oliver is equal parts sexy and pathetic.

Why do men, even *grown* men, always make that stupid little-boy face when they're coming? A few weeks after I turned fifteen, my stepdad and I started fucking. I look at the headboard to avoid making eye-contact.

"Yeah, Jesse. Just like that."

Jesse? Really? Dwight used to call me that, and Daddy before him. Only, I liked it coming from them.

I ride Oliver a little longer. Not too long. Fifteen seconds. Maybe twenty. Until a look of panic sweeps across his face.

"Oh God!" He shoves me off with one hand and reaches between his legs with the other.

Four swift motions. Semen squirts onto the sheets.

Great. I wanted to be fucked, and now I have been.

I almost laugh, but Oliver's expression is that of an abused puppy and I can't bring myself to do anything but pet him. "It's okay." My tone jizzes reassurance. "It was good for me too. Really. These things happen..."

But it isn't *okay*. It's like showing up at a yoga class and finding out the teacher is a no-show. Or driving all the way to your dealer's only to discover that he's been arrested—again—and your supply is cut off.

"Look," I tell Oliver, "no hard feelings, but I'm gonna go."

"Stay."

For once, I'm grateful for boundaries. "Remember, we agreed. Just fucking."

"Can I see you again?"

Is he kidding with this shit?

"I think that might be too relationshippy," I say, pretending our terrible sex isn't the reason for my refusal.

It's a relief to get back to my car, where I can finally let my laughter out. I giggle and guffaw and chortle and chuckle until it doesn't seem funny anymore. Then, I beat the steering wheel with my fists and yell until I'm hoarse. But I don't let myself cry.

≉ 6 ≉

Within an hour, I'll be slurping straight from the bottle, but, since it's only my first drink of the night, I haven't yet turned into a catastrophe. Friday April thirteenth—unlucky and un-sober. Or, maybe, an auspicious beginning to a new and different way of life.

I don't need AA. My problem isn't alcohol. It's coke. As long as I stay away from that, I'll be fine. Besides, I don't feel like going to a women's meeting tonight and, after Wednesday's debacle, the last thing I need is to run into the cardigan-wearing condom-klutz.

I swivel around on my barstool—martini in hand—and survey Arnie's Alehouse for prospects.

A tall Asian guy with an inviting smile is talking to some woman—probably his wife or girlfriend—and, while I'm not above hooking up with someone who's taken (in the bathroom, while their significant other waits, patiently, and cluelessly, for them to return), it isn't my first choice. There's a scruffy-bearded, beer-bellied, flannel-wearing fifty-something who can't stop eye-fucking me. Pass. I like older guys, but not if they've let themselves go. This dude has a Ketchup stain on his t-shirt.

Before I can despair about the lack of prospects, I spot five well-muscled former frat brothers in Delta Psi t-shirts and *Men in Black* shades striding through the swinging double doors.

The tall one lifts his sunglasses and winks in my direction. So what if it's the wrong time of year, and day, and weather, to be wearing shades? I see those sexy green irises and feel a familiar flutter rise up from within.

Will he approach me? Should I approach him?

I pretend to be interested in the drink in my hand, the game on TV, the conversation of the couple sitting next to me. Are they really talking about *traffic*?

Careful, Jess. Play it cool.

Ever since Dwight gave me my first beer, alcohol has been my lubricant. One drink and I'm ready. Willing. Pliant.

It takes fifteen minutes for the stranger with the slightly crooked smile, shaded emerald eyes, and frat-boy t-shirt to approach. From his trying-to-be-cocksure swagger, I can tell that, like me, he's a pretender.

"Hello."

"I like your shirt."

"Do you?"
"Are you in a fraternity?"
He smiles. "I used to be. We're way past our UPenn years, but, sometimes, when we get together, nostalgia wins out."
"So, you're nostalgic...?"
"You're not?"
No. More like tormented by the past.
I lean toward him, drop my voice an octave. "I can be..."
"About what?"
"About tonight—if you play your cards right." It's a great response. The kind of response I'd never think of sober.
He takes his glasses off, revealing those piercing green eyes again, and I notice that his lashes are striking, and oddly feminine. Women pay a fortune to have lashes like his.
"I'm Patrick."
"Jessica."
He grins. "Like the rabbit."
"As in Roger?"
"Is there any other one?"
"I guess not," I concede. I don't feel like Jessica Rabbit. I'm all angles and edges, whereas she was downright voluptuous. Still, I like to think we both ooze sex. "Your friends seem nice."
Patrick's former frat-brothers are staring. I wave across the room. They wave back. I'm glad I decided to take the train down to Center City to get out of my Mt. Airy enclave and meet someone new to do something old.
"Wanna join us?" Patrick asks.
I raise an eyebrow. I'm not above the occasional group thing, but *five* guys is three too many.
"For a drink," he clarifies.
I drain the contents of my martini. "Sounds great."
I'm no fool. He's buying, and I'm broke.
Within a couple minutes, I discover that the five former frat-guys have long-since moved out of the area—Patrick lives in Delaware—but come back to Philly at least one weekend a year to reclaim lost aspects of themselves. And Patrick was right. He and his matching-shirt-wearing crew are nostalgic.
"Remember the time..." is an almost common refrain.

"Remember the time we stole wood from that guy's lawn on a camping trip in the Catskills and he came outside with a rifle and threatened to shoot us?"

"Remember the time the basement flooded and Ruiz started crying?"

Ruiz pipes up. "You'd have cried too if your box full of signed Michael memorabilia got ruined."

"Pussy."

"Michael?" I ask.

Patrick traces my thigh with his fingers. "Jordan."

I lean in so close I can see each individual lash, long and lush and supermodel gorgeous. "Remember the time you met a hot girl in a bar and took her back to your hotel room?"

My green-eyed guy leans in and kisses me. I resist the urge to press my body against his, and, instead, lean back to give him a view of my wonder-bra'ed tits and yoga-toned body.

"Get a room!" Ruiz quips.

"I already have one," Patrick replies. "We're planning on using it."

Before we can make our escape though, the "brothers" insist we join them at a club.

"It wouldn't be a Delta Psi weekend if we didn't *all* go," Joe says.

Patrick looks at me.

I don't need convincing. Dancing is essentially clothed, vertical sex. "I'm in."

"Good." Chaz—a Rubenesque white guy with the jaundiced skin of an alcoholic and bigger boobs than mine—makes a phone call and, within minutes, the six of us are climbing into a dingy yellow cab.

"Why didn't you call Uber?" I ask as I hurtle across the Delta Psi brothers and crash to the floor.

Does our driver even have a license?

"Chaz likes this asshole!" Ruiz shouts down at me.

I scramble off the floor and into Patrick's lap. "Where are we going?"

The driver screeches to a halt, and I tumble down again. "Here!"

Amidst much laughing, Patrick half-carries, half-drags me out of the car.

"Dude, your driver sucks." Joe says.

"Naha!" Chaz protests. "Akmal and I are like this."

He intertwines his fingers while the frat guy whose name I can't remember, even though we were *just* introduced, leans over beside the curb, and inhales and exhales several times to keep from getting sick.

"Go ahead!" he calls after us as we head inside the dimly-lit downtown Philadelphia dance club. "I'm right behind you!"

Evidently, we've arrived in the middle of a girls-gone-wild dance contest. Onstage, bootees of all shapes and sizes gyrate amidst boos and cheers and shouted obscenities. For the most part, it's college girls looking to let loose, but there are a few older, sadder contestants.

"Fuck!" Ruiz points at a completely naked voluptuous thirty-something blonde with a porn star body and vacant, glazed-over expression. She's dancing—off-beat—to music that's as obvious as her insecurities.

Music make you lose control...
Lights (Flashin')
Sound (Crashin')
Minds (Blowin')
Body (Rockin')
Eyes (Lockin')
Lips (Touchin')
Hearts (Pumpin')
Pressure (Risin')
Breathes (Takin')
Rump (Shakin')
Music (Makin')
Lose (Control)

Behind her outward exhibitionism lies a wellspring of pain.

Patrick does a double-take.

The nameless frat guy, his skin far less green, comes up behind me, shaking his head. "That's pathetic," he scoffs.

I don't say anything. How can I? I see myself in her.

"I'm in love!" Chaz sprints toward the stage, and away from the rest of us, intent on wooing the naked stranger with his slurred speech and man-boobs.

Patrick turns to me. "Wanna dance?"

"Hell yes!"

We dance so hard and long and fast that I forget about sobriety and sponsors and broken promises and unrealized dreams. So what if I've lived and relived this same night more times than I can count? It's exciting every time.

"Having fun?" Patrick enfolds me in his arms.

I look up into his lush green eyes with their almost braidable lashes and let the press of my lips against his articulate my answer.

It's Chaz who initiates our quest for drugs. For once, I'm not even thinking about amping up my chemical obliteration with anything harder than alcohol. Patrick is enough.

Still, I've never been one to say no to a little weed, or a line or two of coke.

"This is gonna be a night to remember!" Even though the object of Chaz's love didn't reciprocate his proclamations of affection, he doesn't seem fazed. He makes a call and, ten minutes later, the same dingy taxi that dropped us off pulls up in front of the club.

"This is my guy," Chaz reminds us. "He'll take care of us."

Patrick turns to me with plaintive eyes. "Look, we don't have to go if you don't want to..."

But I want to. Even if I didn't, I'm not about to stand in the way of anyone's attempt to recapture their lost youth. I slide into the cab. The rest of the Delta Psi guys pile in behind me.

"Drogas. Ten-nes drogas? Don da estes drogas?" Chaz asks the driver.

"Why's he speaking Spanish?" Joe whispers.

The other Delta Psi guy (I really should ask him his name, but I've let it go too long and asking now would make me look like an asshole), whispers back, "Because he's a dumb shit."

"Mooch-ohs drogas." Chaz mimes rolling a joint.

The cabbie rolls his eyes and explains—in English—that he's Middle Eastern.

I settle against Patrick's chest, pressing my body into his so I won't fall. He holds me as we drive past dilapidated buildings and women standing on street corners. After a while, the bright lights and buildings turn into back alleys and crumbling complexes—bricks missing, graffiti on the walls. Incomplete artwork. I study the streak of black spray-paint on the side of a fire-singed apartment building. It looks as if someone was interrupted in the process of scrawling his name. I make out a *V*. Or is it half a *W*? Our cab slows to a crawl. The driver clears his throat—the raspy, hollow rattling of a former smoker.

Patrick nudges me. "Look."

From amidst the shadows, a skin-and-bones impression of a man sprints toward us and skitters to a stop mere seconds before colliding with the bright yellow taxi. From my vantage point behind the rolled-up glass, I watch the dark skeleton with bulging, blood-rimmed eyes appraise us appraising him.

This isn't a house in the suburbs where we'll score some pot or coke or a few tabs of E. I'm with strangers in a crack den in Northeast Philadelphia. The skeleton-man shouts a few incomprehensible Spanish words into the darkness.

Apparently, our Middle Eastern cabdriver has taken us to Spanish-speaking drug dealers after all. He shuts off the engine and extinguishes the headlights.

Silence pervades.

Chaz gets out.

The rest of us don't move.

"I'm sorry about this." Patrick clutches me tighter. I let him—not because I'm nervous, but because I'm desperate to be held.

"Hey, Dude, move the fuck over." The seating situation—six people in a cramped cab—is starting to test Joe's patience. Or, maybe, it's just easier to be angry than scared.

Ruiz buries his head in his hands.

From somewhere in the distance, we hear the belligerent shouting of a pink-faced, drunken ex Delta Phi. "Are you fucking kidding me? You motherfucking, cock-sucking son of a bitch!"

Everyone freezes—except me. I get out of the cab and stride toward the yelling.

"Chaz?"

He's standing in front of what looks like a 1920s speak-easy, facing off the anorexic drug-runner while a disembodied arm holds a bag out through a round window in a small shed.

"You're a fucking cheat!"

The skeleton-man appears scared, but resolute.

"What's wrong?" I ask.

"This *asshole*," Chaz spits out the word, "wants to charge me two hundred for three grams."

"Cuanto cuestan estes drogas?" I took Spanish until the twelfth grade. It was required.

The man's eyes dart to the window, then back to us, making me wonder who's more afraid—me or the drug-runner. "Doscientos dolares."

"No. Es muy caro. Nos queremos pagan–" I pause. I've bought coke and E and shrooms, but never crack. Plus, while I may be an addict, I'm not well-versed in the nuances of narcotics acquisition. I have my usual dealer (Markus), who I trust enough to pay whatever he charges. Or—and this is a more common scenario—I use whatever the guy I'm currently fucking is willing to share, which mostly amounts to coke and weed.

"What should it cost?" I whisper.

Luckily, the drunk Delta has the presence of mind to murmur his answer, rather than shouting it. "A hundred bucks."

A steadying arm slips around my waist. Patrick has left the taxi to come and stand bravely,by my side. Now, if I'm raped or murdered, I'll have company.

"Nos queremos pagan sesenta dólares," I bargain.

"Cicento cinquenta," the drug-runner counters.

"Sesenta y cinco."

"Ciento y treinta," he insists.

"No. Es muy caro."

"Okay. One hundred, but no lower." Apparently, the man's English is better than he let on. He catches himself and reverts back to his native tongue. "Esto es el precio menor."

"Ciento," I agree. "Es el bueno precio."

I tell Chaz to give the man a hundred dollars. He hands over the cash. The emergent arm relinquishes its bag.

"You were awesome!" Chaz says as we climb into the cab.

"Thanks."

Despite my upscale Main Line upbringing and skanky Skipper-doll appearance, I've never shied away from sketchy situations. But, even for me, buying crack in a Spanish-speaking Kensington crack-den isn't a common occurrence.

"This is some good shit," Chaz croons. "I can't wait to get back to the hotel." Even though he lives in Jersey, he's staying at the same hotel as the others. Part of their plan is to resurrect the togetherness of their UPenn days. "Jess, you gonna do crack with us?"

I shake my head. "I think I'll pass."

If I do crack, there's no pretending I'm anything other than a lost soul.

Patrick leans over. "You sure? I think I want to try it."

"If you want to try it, you should." Far be it from me to get between a man and his drugs.

Our cabbie pulls into their hotel parking lot and the five Delta Psis spill out onto the pavement in a drunken, disorganized heap. Patrick looks from me—waiting in the cab, the door still open—to Chaz and his baggie, then back to me again.

"Do whatever you want," I tell him. "I don't care. Really."

He puts a hand on the dented yellow roof so he can lean in and kiss me goodbye. "Can I see you tomorrow?"

It's an exquisite offer. "Of course."

As the driver restarts the engine, Patrick shouts so loudly that strangers stop and stare and his friends move away and pretend not to know him. "You're the one, Jessica! You complete me and give me wings!"

I stifle a laugh with one hand as I wave out my rolled-down window with the other.

The driver sighs and shakes his head. "Where do you live?"

"You can drop me off at 30th Street Station."

I can't afford cab fare all the way back to Mt. Airy, but he explains that Chaz and the others have put it on their tab.

"Really?"

In AA, they tell us you are who you associate with, and Patrick's friends are stand-up guys, which means he and I could actually have something. Eager to get home and go to sleep so it can be tomorrow, I give the cabbie my address. As he drives west on I-76, I keep the window down, so the wind in my face will slap me awake each time my eyes start to close.

Thirty minutes later, the driver breaks hard, sending me crashing against my door. "Here."

I get out in front of the Lincoln Drive Apartments, climb up the stairs to the second floor, weave my way down the hall, unlock my door, crawl, fully clothed, into bed, and fall asleep before my head hits the pillow.

It's not until I wake that I realize that Patrick and I forgot to exchange numbers.

7

Since my night with Oliver, I've been ignoring April's calls and letting her texts go unanswered. On the bright side, since my almost-night with Patrick, I've made sure to fuck all the men I meet before saying goodbye. It's not long before whatever shreds of self-esteem I'd amassed from my brief stint of sobriety are eviscerated. The days and nights accumulate. At first, I manage to make it through my shifts sober before going out and getting shitfaced, but that doesn't last. After a trip to the intersection of Fifth Street and Carpenter to see Markus and fortify my supplies, I'm doing coke in the Free Café bathroom and smoking weed in my car whenever I can get away for a fifteen-minute break.

I tell myself this time won't be like all the others. I'm still showing up to work—almost on time—and I'm not completely miserable.

Last night, April 27th, exactly two weeks after Patrick opted to get high instead of having sex with me, I met someone. Rocko and I locked eyes in an alley while doing lines of coke off the lid of a garbage can, and, despite the differences in our upbringings and experiences, there was an unmistakable resonance between us.

Rocko is a heavily-tattooed South Philly Italian with a goatee and a small scar on his lower lip that he got during a barroom brawl. His lip-scar is my favorite thing about him.

"Must've been a bad fight," I tell him as I trace the raised white flesh with my tongue.

Rocko smiles, the scar stretching into a long, menacing gash. "Not for me. The other guy's in a wheelchair now."

He mashes his mutilated mouth against my unmarred one and something about the intensity of his kiss assures me that he craves the high I can provide even more than the drugs laid out on the table in front of us.

The last guy who made me feel this wanted was Dwight. And I screwed it up.

A few days before my eighteenth birthday, I videotaped my stepdad and myself doing it—doggy style, so both our faces were staring directly at the hidden nanny cam. I was starting college, and, even though I'd only enrolled part-time at a school that was less than twenty miles away, I wanted to live closer to the Temple campus. To get away from the suburbs and the person I'd been in high school.

And that meant leaving Dwight behind—with Chloe.

So, I made several copies of the tape and gave one to him on the way out the door.

"If you touch her," I warned, "I'll have you arrested for molesting me."

"I didn't molest you! You wanted it!"

My stepdad was right. But teenage pussy was teenage pussy and, I felt sure, he'd acquired a taste.

Chloe was a good girl. Not like me. I didn't want him corrupting her.

"Just keep your dick in your pants."

He called me a whore.

Burning the bridge of our relationship created an inferno that singed all the way down to my soul, but I owed it to Chloe to do one thing right as a sister. Still, I wanted him to tell me I was crazy—that he could never want Chloe because I was the girl of his dreams. Instead, he let me go and our love went up in flames.

I have the sneaking suspicion that, whenever I've called to ask him for money, or to bail me out of jail, or to pick me up after an angry ex has left me outside, stranded, it's been fear, rather than affection, that's compelled Dwight to come to my rescue.

Rocko's apartment is a dingy, windowless shithole, so, when he finds out I'm about to be evicted for not paying rent, he invites himself to move in with me. "It's a problem with a self-evident solution."

I accept his offer and wad of crumpled cash. I'm not about to call Mom, or April, or even Dwight, for help.

"I'm glad you came to me with this and we could conversate about the issue from a goal-oriented outlook. I know what we have is new, Jess, but fiscal comingling is an essential component of any successful romantic partnership, and, if I'm being entirely honest, I was looking for an excuse to vacate my current domicile anyway."

That's the thing about Rocko. He uses words like *vacate* and *conversate* and *domicile*, and phrases such as *fiscal comingling*. When we went to the Men's Warehouse to buy him a suit for his former cellmate's wedding, he stumped all the retail salesmen by referring to the discount clothing store as a "haberdashery." Then, in the same conversation, his grammar slips to a third-grade level and he starts talking about bitches and hoes and how he "ain't got no use" for his "boy down the block no more" because "that motherfucker owes me some cheddar." Plus, I've never seen him read anything more complex than an Arby's menu.

I peer at my new live-in boyfriend over a Raisin Bran cereal box. "Rocko, you are a dichotomy."

"What's that? Some sort of slang for asshole? So, I forgot to take out the fucking trash. Babe, you've got to reprioritize. Life is a ferocious and tempestuous animal, unwilling to be tamed. Grab me a Corona, will ya?"

My neighbors, who have never approved of me anyway, look askance at Rocko and me whenever we enter or exit the building. Not that we go out much.

I go to work sometimes, but I'm not sure how Rocko earns his income. One afternoon, I come home to the smell of burning plastic. He hands me a pipe.

I start to say no, but Rocko informs me we're all out of dope. "All we have is crack and H."

I'm terrified of needles. I could go out and pick something else up, but this is free, and I barely have enough cash for groceries. The box of Frosted Flakes and container of milk I bought last week are down to crumbs and an inch of frothy after-swill. It's another three days until I get paid, and my work attendance has been spotty.

I take a hit—something I swore I'd never do. Memories of Patrick and the crack he offered and telling myself, if I said yes, I'd be a lost soul surface. I take another. They recede.

Besides, I don't feel lost. I feel found.

The next two weeks are swallowed up in getting stoned and having sex (when Rocko isn't too high to get it up). Occasionally, I go to work. Mostly, I call out sick.

"How come smoking makes me lazy?" I wonder. "And snorting gives me so much energy?"

Rocko rouses himself long enough to reply. "Different conduits alter the nature of the same chemical compound." His own laziness makes sense. He's on H, and, possibly, something else. He was in the bathroom for a long time, and, when he came out, he looked like someone had taken a cheese grater to his ambition.

I tell my boss I have mono. "I'm *so* tired. Getting myself to work feels impossible."

He's empathetic. His daughter had mono in high school. "Just rest," he advises. "That's all you can do. And, Jess..."

"Yeah?"

"We're here when you're ready."

Rocko's friends become permanent fixtures in my—well, now, *our*—apartment. One sports a series of teardrop tattoos. Another's face is a labyrinth of jagged lacerations. The last one has a glass eye. He takes it out to show me, revealing a hollow, cavernous socket.

I throw up on the living room floor.

These men traipse in and out of my apartment, but I don't mind. I like being surrounded by people who are too fucked up to judge me.

* * *

It's Tuesday, June 12th—nine days before the official start of summer. Even though we haven't talked in two months, April still calls almost every day. Her messages clutter my voicemail.

A snore.

Rocko is passed out on the couch.

Tank, his friend with the three, delicate teardrops below his left eye, grins. "Motherfucker can't hold his liquor."

I take a sip and pass the bottle.

Tank doesn't drink. Instead, he looks me over, his sly smile reaching all the way to his crying eyes, and says, "How about you and me go into the bedroom?"

I glance at Rocko. His head is hanging off the side of the sofa, a puddle of drool beside him. My live-in crack connection isn't waking up any time soon. And, even if he does, it's not like we've had the exclusivity conversation.

I take a hit. Pass the pipe. This time, Tank partakes.

"Okay. What the hell?"

Tank is everything his nickname suggests. I ride him like a mechanical bull at a county fair—for fun and to prove my prowess. When it's over, he hoists me in the air with one hand and plonks me down on the bed beside him.

Happy teardrops and a scarless smile. "That was good. Rocko's right. You're something special."

Shit. I forgot about Rocko.

"We better get out there before he wakes up." I smooth out the wrinkles in my shirt.

My hard-bodied accomplice isn't worried. He saunters into his jeans.

"Shhh..." I put a finger to my lips, but, when I emerge from our shared bedroom, my "boyfriend" is standing by the door, all signs of drool and drunkenness gone. I expect him to rage—to hit me, to hit his friend, to threaten us, to storm out, to kick Tank out, or, at the very least, to let fly a string of expletives, like Dwight used to do whenever he caught me stepping out. Instead, Rocko holds out his hand and Tank deposits several bills of various denominations into his open palm.

I want to hurl as I realize what has happened. Instead, I tell my pimp and my patron that I have to go.

Tank shrugs. "Okay. See you later."

"Bring us back a pizza," Rocko adds.

It's 12:47 on a Tuesday afternoon. I drive a few miles down the road to the Germantown one o'clock Daily Lunchtime Liberation Meeting. The one o'clock meeting is teeming with former and current marines—guys on leave, guys awaiting deployment, and guys who've done their time and been honorably discharged but haven't found civilian employment yet. These former drunks have discipline, integrity and courage. Unlike me, they can be counted on.

As I sit in my chair, trembling, trying not to think about the fact that I reek of beer, singed plastic, and sex, I don't pay attention to the gripes and gratitudes of the sober, cocksure maritime men.

I'm a woman with a mission of my own.

I wait until the end to share. Not the very end—in case I raise my hand and don't get called on—but second to last. When it's my turn, I use my three minutes to explain the situation back at my apartment and beg my surrounding AA strangers for help. Meetings aren't supposed to be a place for recruitment, but I'm a user. Besides, I don't know what else to do.

After the Serenity Prayer and the Seventh Tradition collection, to which I'm too strapped to contribute, three of the youngest, biggest, marines approach. "You want these assholes out?"

Because I can't bring myself to lock eyes with these defenders of corps and country, I look at the floor and answer through clenched teeth. "Please."

"Lead the way," the tall one says.

When the marines follow me home, I'm surprised to find that, despite all their barroom shenanigans, male bravado, and aggregate prison time, neither Rocko nor Tank is reckless enough to tangle with trained infantry men. Or maybe I'm not worth fighting for.

My boyfriend and his friend put all their stuff into two oversized trash bags, then head off in their respective cars—probably to Tank's place, although I'll never know.

The shortest, beefiest marine (who is six feet tall and probably about twelve percent body fat) stays with me while the other two take a trip to Killian's Hardware store to get a new lock apparatus. I hadn't even thought about changing my locks.

"Thanks," I say as soon as Steve and I are alone.

He appraises me thoughtfully. "Anything else?"

"Yes."

Steve follows me into the bathroom, where I flush my stash down the toilet. "Took me a while to kick the habit too." His expression is as soft as his body is hard. "Just keep trying. You'll get it. We all do, eventually—if it doesn't get us first."

When the others get back, they make short work of the lock-swapping process.

"You're good at that," I tell the tallest one as he wields his screwdriver with the precision of an expert.

"He better be." The other guy takes a swig of Diet Coke—my only payment to these men for rescuing me from Rocko, the Tank and whatever flesh-pedaling arrangement I'd inadvertently gotten myself into. "This son of a bitch is a combat engineer."

"Impressive."

As soon as they're out the door, I call April.

My sponsor isn't even mad I've been ignoring her. "I'm glad you reached out. And that you're alive."

We talk for hours. Well, I talk. She listens.

"This time," I tell her, "it'll be different. This is my bottom. It can't get any worse."

Three hours after we hang up, I crawl into bed, confident that I'm done with drugs forever. Yet, despite all my sincere promises, my early-morning resolve is nonexistent. I'm drunk before noon, high an hour after.

8

My next "boyfriend" is Luke. We meet doing ecstasy at a rave in a seedy section of Trenton. He is beautiful, passionate, and creative. I fall for him immediately. Well, for his potential. Luke is going to be a world-renowned poet someday. He's only dealing so he can earn enough to go to school for his MFA. Okay, so he hasn't actually applied to any grad programs yet, but he reads me some of his poetry, and it's impressive.

A firefly alights in the darkness, illuminating everything, until it extinguishes itself…

After only three blissful days together, my intuition tells me we're destined for each other. And, even though it's less than a week since the Rocko situation, I find myself practically living at Luke's place.

I thought you were coming back to meetings, April texts.

I will, I mentally cross my fingers to make my words a loophole, as opposed to a lie. *I've been really busy.*

You know, Jess, you can't be too dumb for the program, but you can be too smart.

I don't care about intellect right now. Not in the face of this overpowering feeling, that begins in my belly and radiates downward to my groin. This freefall into adoration. Dating a dealer is perfect. A continual high.

Be careful, my intuition whispers. *He's on heroin.*

I push away the paranoia. Luke only uses H to deepen his artistic expression. He's not hooked or anything. He's enterprising and ambitious. Almost every night, he adds a stack of cash to the duffel in his closet.

A week and a half into what feels like love, I crawl into bed beside the man of my dreams, nestle against him, and thank a god I don't believe in for letting someone want me.

Dwight's words alight in the darkness of my mind.

"Face it, Jesse, after what you've done, no one's ever gonna love you—except me."

I haven't told Luke about my past, or the part I played in it. I will. Eventually. He's not the type to judge. Maybe, I'll tell him tonight.

Like Dwight, Luke sees me and accepts me as I am. I see him too, although I don't see the tourniquet, expertly-tied around his arm. As I curl up next to his strong, sinewy body and tell him my aspirations—

ones he's heard before, and new ones, fueled by today's lines and the joint I smoked earlier—I fail to notice that his face is ashy and gray.

"I have a secret," I say. "Something I've never told anyone. When I was fifteen, I seduced my stepdad."

It takes a long time to realize that Luke's not listening. Even longer to comprehend that he hasn't simply fallen asleep.

"Hey, I'm talking to you! Did you hear what I said?" I shake him, but he doesn't wake.

A needle spills off the bed, onto the floor. The guillotine of fear severs my body from my mind. Thoughts, panic reverberating, I somehow manage to stumble to my cell and dial 9-1-1.

The police come immediately. They don't ask questions. They've been to Luke's place more times than they can count. One of them tells me—maybe callously, maybe honestly—that it was only a matter of time before Luke died of a heroin overdose.

"Your boyfriend was a nice kid." His face is blank—unaffected. "But a lost cause. A good girl like you should find a man you can depend on."

People always assume that, because of my light eyes and blonde hair and suburban inculcation, I'm the type of girl my mother raised me to be.

Mrs. Evangeline Carrington (formerly Mrs. Evangeline Leonard) was the kind of mother they feature in cheesy after-school specials. She said things like "It's God's will," always had dinner on the table at six, and never left the house without makeup. Plus, she taught me manners. Maybe that's why, when Dwight and I first started fucking, I asked him to "please" not put it in too deep. And, when he capitulated, I made sure to say "Thank you."

I didn't write him any notes though. Real etiquette—the kind Mom taught me—demands written *Thank you*s.

"I don't understand." How can Luke—who made me feel alive in too many ways to enumerate—be dead? "He was fine earlier."

The other cop tells me they don't need me at the station. "What happened here isn't a crime," he says. "Just one of the casualties of a life improperly lived."

The officers let the paramedics deal with Luke's corpse while they take off in their Trenton PD cruiser—heading to Wawa, no doubt, for something caffeinated to get them through the nightshift. A legal stimulant without stigma or consequences.

I remain riveted in Luke's bedroom until the paramedics take his body away and, once again, I am utterly alone. Then, I slump to the floor and cry a lifetime of accumulated tears for all the men who have left me—some through death, most through desertion—and the one I left, even though I loved him.

Love.

My feelings for Luke are still a lifetime shy of their expiration date. Yet, I go into his closet, find his Nike duffel, walk out of his apartment, and never look back.

9

I'm on an unfamiliar rooftop, staring down at the City of Brotherly Love. The world is expansive and I am at the apex of existence. It's been a week since Luke was taken from me. Long enough to move on to the next person, the next party. The next line. Trying, always trying, to forget.

Through the kaleidoscope of my eyes, the people below me are simultaneously magnificent and insignificant. They wander aimlessly through the labyrinth that is life.

I exist outside of the kaleidoscope. I am a bird with gorgeous, Technicolor wings—big blue, purple, and magenta ailerons. I spread my naked arms, unencumbered by excess fabric.

On this hot, summer night, I'm wearing a slinky black camisole that an old boyfriend gave me as a gift. He meant it to be lingerie, but I don't confine its sexiness to bedrooms. That would be a waste. Lingerie only ever ends up discarded on the floor.

Everyone stares. They can't help it.

"What's she doing?"

"I dunno. Who'd she come with?"

Who did I come with? I didn't catch his name. We met earlier tonight at the 30th Street Station.

I took the train in to Center City to avoid the possibility of a DUI and he'd been heading back to his place—a high-rise apartment with a vast urban view.

That's where we are. The roof of the guy's building. His roommate is hosting a party and a dozen or so of us have left the confines of the cramped, aircondition-less two-bedroom to breathe in the fresh Philly air. Only, that's not the real reason I'm here.

When he asked if I felt like getting lit, I took the proffered purple pill without a moment's hesitation. It was the same, bright, exotic hue as the tips of my feathers.

I didn't have the feathers then. The pill transformed me.

From the street below, an unfamiliar girl stares up at me, trying to assassinate me with envy. She doesn't know that she too can be a bird. I want to tell her, but she's too far away and words dissolve in my mouth like sublingual LSD.

There's another girl too. This one is standing behind me. She has hair like Chloe's and the same disapproving smile as my mother. She wants to stop me from flying. That's why I'm not going to tell her what I plan to do.

She can't stop staring. The smile is gone now. Her face is a blank slate.

I inch closer to the roof's steep edge. Look down. The jealous one has been joined by more people. They all look up at me. Some are willing me to soar. Others want to clip my wings.

"You can't!" I shout at all the naysayers.

I imagine them sitting in Church, so mired in stories of crucifixion and resurrection that they ignore the possibility of experiencing heaven here on earth.

A shock of recognition. A familiar face in the crowd. I see a man I know. And, then, just that quickly, he's too far away to make out who he is.

A glimpse of dark hair with a shocking streak of white.

I inhale. A deep, yogic breath that descends down into my diaphragm. The sun has set. There's no use saluting it. So, I simply exhale. Then, I spread my wings and fly.

Part II

Pose

Downward Facing Dog (Adho Mukha Svanasana)

Begin on your hands and knees on your yoga mat, with your knees directly underneath your hips, and your hands slightly in front of your shoulders. Curl your toes under, pressing your hands firmly on your mat. Then, straighten your arms and legs, lengthen your tailbone, and broaden your back. Your body should form an upside down V-shape.

Prayer

Third Step Prayer

God, I offer myself to Thee — to build with me and to do with me as Thou wilt. Relieve me of the bondage of self, that I may better do Thy will. Take away my difficulties, that victory over them may bear witness to those I would help of Thy Power, Thy Love, and Thy Way of life. May I do Thy will always!

Promise

"We have found much of heaven and we have been rocketed into a fourth dimension of existence of which we had not even dreamed." (*Alcoholics Anonymous Big Book*, p. 25)

Step Two:

Came to believe that a power greater than ourselves could restore us to sanity. (Gate Pose)

≠ 10 ≠

I drift in and out of consciousness for three days before finally opening my eyes and keeping them open. Dingy hospital gray walls. A series of monitors. The smell of antiseptic isn't so much evidence of cleanliness as a haphazard attempt to eradicate the stench of decay. On the wall, there's a poster. *Jefferson Memorial Hospital,* it says, *Honesty is the first chapter in the book of wisdom.*

I attempt to move my head, only it won't budge. So, I shift my eyes sideways and catch sight of a metal brace in my peripheral vision. When I open my mouth to call for assistance, a shockwave of pain erupts in my extremities and all that emerges is a scream.

A nurse hurries in, presses something I can't see (a button, maybe, or a lever), adjusts something else. The pain begins to subside.

"Morphine?"

She doesn't understand. My voice is rusty with disuse.

"What?"

"Morphine," I repeat. I've had morphine before—in a different, recreational, context. I recognize its blissful oblivion.

The nurse stands by my bedside, her lips tight and twisted. "You almost died." From the way she says it, I get the impression she'd have preferred that outcome over this one.

"I did?" I always thought nearly dying would be the kind of thing a person would remember.

"Yes."

The last thing I recall is spreading my wings and soaring—like an angel, or a peacock, or a raven.

"What happened? What day is it?"

"It's July 11th, 2018. You jumped off a roof—because you were *high*—fractured a leg, dislocated a shoulder, punctured a lung, broke two of your toes and sprained an ankle. You had massive internal bleeding, a serious concussion, and a bruised sternum."

She pauses, to let the information sink in and remorse rise from my subconscious to my surface. It doesn't. I'm on morphine. Everything is okay.

"We can't know what internal or cerebral damage you sustained because the doctors had to put you into a medically induced coma so they could give the swelling in your brain time to go down."

"Oh." It's a stupid response. Again, I blame the morphine.

"I'm going to get a doctor to talk to you more about your situation."

"I'd rather you get me something to eat. I'm starving."

She furrows her brow and puckers her lips so tight I start to wonder if she's constipated. But I don't ask. She already hates me, and the last thing I want to do is piss off the person responsible for dispensing my narcotics. Still, it's unfair for someone whose hair looks like she dipped it in a vat of orange Kool-Aid to judge me for my choices.

"I'll see what I can do."

A few minutes later, she surprises me by coming back not only with a doctor, but a peanut butter and jelly sandwich, and a carton of generic two percent milk.

"It's not a meal time," she informs me. "Dinner is at 5:30. Until then, this is the best I can do."

"What time is it now?"

"3:15." She hands me the sandwich. Big mistake. I ignore the doctor as he prattles on about complex fractures, concussions, the dangers of addiction, and my need for "serious physiological, and psychological, intervention" and focus my attention on the unhealthiest, gooiest, most processed, most delicious thing I've ever eaten.

"Do you understand, Ms. Leonard?" The doctor glares at me, his expression as exasperated as the nurse's. It's clear from both their frowns that he's asked this question before. Multiple times.

"Of course," I reply, my mouth sticky with brown and purple goo. "Do I look like an idiot?"

He has the good grace not to answer.

11

I want to shut my eyes, but it's too late. April's already caught me looking at her.

Yesterday, after the doctor finished his lecture, the nurse asked for an emergency contact, and, against my better judgment, and under the influence of pain reliever and peanut butter, I gave her April's information.

When the nurse called, April's phone was off. She and Howie had taken the girls to Six Flags and, when they got home, it was so late they all went straight to bed. It wasn't until six a.m. this morning that April turned her cell back on and listened to her messages.

She drove straight here.

I wince.

"Is it the pain?"

I want to say yes, so April will tell the nurse to administer another shot of morphine.

I really am a fucking addict. I'm lying in a hospital bed after having almost died, and all I can think about is how much I want to get high.

But I know this pain demands to be felt, so I let myself be more vulnerable than I've been in a while. "Can you teach me?"

"Teach you what?"

"How to be sober."

April grins. "You already know how. One day and one moment at a time."

"One breath." The words come out in a wheeze.

"Exactly."

We inhale and exhale together. A shockwave of pain courses through me. I close my eyes to block out the thousand stabbing knives slashing through my flesh, digging deep into my bones, and twisting—hard.

My sponsor takes my hand. "Close your eyes. It'll help."

As usual, she's right. I imagine I'm in Corpse Pose at the end of a long, depleting yoga class and will myself to do as Sati advises and "let my tension dissipate."

I should have died—would have, if not for the fact that I alighted on an awning before rolling off and landing on the sidewalk.

"Good," April coaxes. "Be in the moment. Focus on your breath."

For once, I do as she instructs. No resistance. Only surrender.

Somehow, my body takes pity on me. I fall asleep again.

* * *

"How long was I out?"

April hasn't moved since 6:48 this morning. "A couple of hours."

"What time is it?"

"A little after nine."

"Aren't Howie and the girls waiting for you?"

"They don't need me right now, Jess. You do."

It's true. I can't remember the last time I let myself acknowledge how much I needed someone other than myself. My insistence on appearing self-sufficient started as a teenager, when I told myself I was more grown-up than I was.

"Does everybody know?"

"You forget the definition of 'anonymous'?"

My eyebrows are the only part of me still capable of moving without pain.

April laughs. "People have been asking. What do you want me to tell them?"

"Tell them not to be idiots and to keep going to meetings."

"So, essentially, the formula for sobriety?"

I try, and fail, to keep self-pity from suffusing my tone. "Guess I'm destined to be another AA cautionary tale."

April reaches out and smoothes the wrinkled covers at my feet. "I think you're destined to be an inspiration."

"How do you figure?"

"The lower you sink, the more miraculous it is when you swim."

A nurse comes in—a different one than the one who lectured me before. I want another peanut butter sandwich, but there's a tray beside the bed with congealed eggs, dry, tasteless-looking toast, and a lump of defrosted hash browns that someone must've delivered while I was asleep.

"You've gotta keep your strength up," the nurse tells me. "Recovery takes a lot of work."

I know she means my body, but I wink at April anyway.

"How you doin' for morphine, sweetie? What's your pain like?"

This time, when April and I lock eyes, I don't wink. Still, she knows what I'm thinking.

"Actually..." My sponsor answers for me. "We need to talk to Jess' doctor about how to manage her medication in a safe way."

The nurse seems confused.

"I'm an addict," I admit. "You asking if I want more morphine is like asking if I want cocaine. Even if I weren't in pain, it'd be almost impossible to say no."

"I'm proud of you," April tells me after the nurse has scurried away in search for my legal drug dispenser.

But I don't feel like talking about how I've just condemned myself to the hell of an untranquilized existence, so I nod toward the tray on the adjustable over-bed table. "That stuff looks inedible."

"How about I go down to the cafeteria and get you a sandwich or something?"

"Peanut butter and jelly?"

"Sure."

"Hey, April..."

"Yeah?"

"Guess I need you after all."

By the time she gets back, I've drifted off again. I don't wake until after the lunch tray has been delivered, but I forego dry chicken, wilted string beans, and too-yellow corn in favor of sweet, gooey processed deliciousness. Rolling great gobs of grape guts and pulverized nuts around inside my mouth transports me back to a time before loss and lust and loneliness robbed me of innocence and, for the first time in a long time, I find myself thinking that, maybe, everything will be okay. Then, the doctor arrives with my chart and his prescription pad and I know it won't. Not if I have to follow through with my resolve to be different.

12

Eight weeks after being released from the hospital, six weeks after discontinuing any pain meds stronger than Tylenol, I drag myself to my first-ever Hatha yoga class.

It's September 12th, the middle of the day, the middle of the week—the time when retirees, the independently wealthy, and the unemployed can indulge themselves with a breathing babysitter. That's essentially what a restorative yoga teacher does, right? Watch her students inhale and exhale for an hour while moving—slowly—from one gentle pose to another.

I've always avoided restorative classes. A commitment-phobe on and off the mat, I'd rather flit from posture to posture than settle in for a more prolonged experience. But my body can't handle anything vigorous yet. I'm still recovering. Besides, I'm avoiding the Satis of the yoga world. They're too ephemeral, too certain of their own, evolved states.

They are a reminder of how far I have fallen.

A pudgy forty-something big-haired brunette named Rhonda stands at the front of the room and reads poetry while we sit in Easy Pose. Her name conjures up images of sexless Jewish women playing mahjong and attending synagogue. Yet, her face is open, her eyes kind. She strikes a match in the pitch-black room and lowers its dwindling flame to a single white votive.

Outside, the sun is shining brightly, but the blackout curtains make it feel as if Serenity isn't just a studio, but an escape.

"Take a deep breath," Rhonda says. "And feel whatever your body is trying to communicate."

Silence washes over me. The tears come. They are the truth I resist telling. They express what I cannot.

"Stay with your breath—and your emotions." She addresses the entire class, but I feel like the teacher is speaking only to me.

I have a sudden urge to crawl into her lap. Instead, I breathe in and out.

Candles burn. The sweet scent of Nag Champa suffuses the air. By the time we get to Child's Pose, my mat is wet with tears.

My body shakes.

It feels so… honest.

I'm grateful for the darkness.

I expected to hate this—after all, I've spent years forcing my feelings to remain inside—but something about letting go is liberating.

Once class is over, after I've dried my eyes, I approach the frumpy, middle-aged teacher.

"Thank you," I tell the unlikely guru. "That was deep."

"What happened?" She gestures toward the boot on my foot, the sling on my arm.

"I took a bad fall," I explain.

When she opens her arms for a hug, Rhonda is as soft and warm as I imagined. Her arms wring out the sponge of me, squeezing a few more tears from what I thought were dehydrated eyes.

She seems to sense that there is more to my story than I am ready—or willing—to divulge. "Keep coming back," she says. "Yoga heals our bodies and our hearts."

It's the same thing they tell me at AA: *Keep coming back.*

"I will," I promise.

And, for once, I mean it.

13

Step one: We admitted we were powerless over cocaine—that our lives had become unmanageable.

I read the words at the top of the page. Below them, I've scribbled April's instructions.

Write about powerlessness.

Write about all the ways life is unmanageable.

The last thing I want to do is acknowledge the truths I've been trying not to face, but my sponsor assures me that the steps are the path—the only path—to lasting transformation.

"They're like asanas in yoga," she tells me. "Each one builds upon the next."

I press my pen into the page.

I am powerless over drugs and alcohol. Once I start, I can't stop. I used to wake up every day and promised myself I wouldn't use. Then, before I knew it, I'd be using. I couldn't help it. No amount of wishing away my alcoholism helped and, no matter how bad the consequences got, I couldn't let go of coke or weed. I even started smoking crack.

Again and again, I've proven to myself that I can't drink without getting drunk, and the last time I got a little high was over a decade ago.

I write about the endless string of broken promises, about days and nights lost to drinking, the catastrophic consequences of my attempts at using moderately, and the relationships sacrificed on the altar of addiction. I write until my wrist cramps and my brain runs out of ink. Then, I sit back in my chair, shake out my hand, and allow my mind to wander.

"If I were your age, I would totally date you." Dwight is leaning back in his recliner.

My eyes are red, my tear ducts raw.

I'm officially a loser. No one has asked me to the ninth-grade dance.

I say nothing.

"Seriously, Jesse, you're beautiful, smart, talented, fun, funny... sexy."

No one else is home. It's just the two of us.

"You think so?" I'm fourteen, but I climb into his lap, as if I were five.

Dwight enfolds me in his strong, fatherly embrace. I nestle close and absorb the comfort. When he kisses me, it's different than the usual peck on the cheek or chaste lips to my forehead. This kiss makes me feel wanted. And uncomfortable.

It wasn't until several months after that solace-imbued dance of lips, five years after he gave me my first beer, that I took Dwight all the way inside me.

Just before, he popped the top on a Sam Adams and held it out for me to take. "It'll help you relax. So you can enjoy it."

And it did. And I did.

I turn my attention back to the page.

I nearly died jumping off a roof when I was high. I've lost every good job I've ever had due to drug use. I'm estranged from my family. I'm broke. I'm incapable of healthy relationships. My last boyfriend was a drug dealer who died of a heroin overdose. The one before him pimped me out to his friend. I've lost my self-respect. One time, when I was tripping on acid, I sold our family dog to a neighbor's kid for fifty bucks, then lied and said he stole the dog out of our yard. His parents grounded him for a week, and I never returned the fifty.

I've had sex with people for money or drugs (or money to buy drugs). Addiction has ruined my life, and, even as I write this, there's a part of me that would give anything to be able to get high right now.

I look down. Words scrawled inside thin blue lines, like prisoners contained between the bars of a jail cell. How is this supposed to make me hate myself less? I want to burrow under the covers and fall asleep and never wake up. I want to snort or smoke or drink my shame away. But escaping isn't an option. This morning, I made a commitment at an AA meeting that I'd stay sober, and it's now 7:30 at night and I'm determined to make it through the day.

Even though I'd rather be rolling a joint, I unroll my yoga mat, sit in Easy Pose, and recall Rhonda's words.

We are a culture of dis-ease. Yet, despite whatever unrest exists beyond the four walls of this yoga room, peace is always available on the mat. Find it here. Internalize it before you have to show up "off the mat."

I close the shutters of my eyelids and transcend the claustrophobia of my apartment. Peace. Ease. I can't feel them. Not now. Not yet. So, instead, I inhale until my lungs overflow with air, then exhale for what feels like an eternity—until I am finally cracked open.

"Daddy, can I have a piece of gum?"

I'm too young to be chewing gum, and he's too old to be chewing it. Nevertheless, my dad hands me two quarters. I drop one in the slot. I'm not strong enough to turn the metal knob on the machine, yet, instead of doing it for me, Daddy takes my tiny hand in his larger one.

Together, we turn.

My dad always made me feel like I was stronger than I was.

I'm fixated on the bright, artificial, intoxicating spheres as they meander down the gumball highway—traveling at the speed of desire.

The first one to come out is white. I put the second quarter in and, together, Daddy and I turn the knob again. A red ball this time. Red is Daddy's favorite too. He lets me have it though. I pop the gumball in my mouth without a thank you. Strange how I always seemed to forget my manners with the man who was never anything but gentle and kind.

Daddy stares at his hard, white orb.

"Aren't you gonna have it?" I ask.

"Well, let's see... Should I or should I save it for later?"

"If you save it for later, can I have it?"

He laughs. "You want everything, don't you Jesse?"

A Cheshire cat grin—teeth stained red with artificial coloring.

"Okay," he concedes. "You can have my piece too."

I skip along beside him, oblivious to the depth of my entitlement and the breadth of his sacrificial love, naively believing that his brand of paternity would be available forever.

I open my eyes. An empty wall in front of me. The urge has passed. It's still early—not yet eight o'clock. Too early to be going to bed. I go anyway. Anything to get through one more sober day.

14

No one warned me that, even after getting sober, the past would cling to me like dirt beneath a gravedigger's fingernails.

"Begin in Child's Pose," Rhonda instructs.

My forehead presses against the mat. My arms outstretch in front of me. I used to hate Child's Pose. It felt so passive. These days, I want to be passive.

My arm is out of its sling, but it still feels weak. I can't yet manage a Downward Dog. Whereas it was once easy to shape my body into an upside-down *V*, I now have to modify the pose by keeping my forearms on the floor.

My entire life feels like a giant modification designed to keep me from hurting myself.

Sobriety is life's Child's Pose. It's been seventy-seven days since my fall off the roof, sixty-five since my release from Jefferson. In the beginning, I was too immobilized—and too demoralized—to deal with anything other than my physical recovery. Plus, for a while, I was on doctor-prescribed, sponsor-administered pain meds. But, now that I've healed from my more serious, leap-induced injuries, now that I have fifty-two days free of any mind-altering substances, I'm free to think about other things—like getting high—which is why I barely do anything other than go to AA and yoga. And, when I do venture someplace else, like a child, I go with a chaperone.

This morning, April picked me up from my apartment and drove me to the grocery store. I have a car. I can drive. Yet, I called my sponsor, my voice thick with fear, and told her I was afraid to get behind the wheel. Not afraid to drive, but of the internal propulsion toward my addiction.

On the way to the grocery, I pass a bar *and* a liquor store. If I make a turn down a familiar side street, I can score drugs from a girl I know who sells for her boyfriend while he's at work at his standing Saturday morning dog walking gig.

Work... I hate that I'm off on disability right now. Hate being labeled "hopeless" even more.

Hopeless. That's what the hospital social worker wrote in my file. Jessica Leonard is hopelessly and clinically depressed, suicidal and co-addicted. Her chances of survival are not good, and her need for relief is urgent and immediate.

I'm not sure why she felt a need to show me what she'd written. Maybe, she figured I was too far gone to care. Or, maybe, she wanted to scare me straight. Stupid her. She didn't realize I'm already afraid. Have been since I was five.

When I tell April I'm terrified of everything, she tells me I'm exactly where I'm supposed to be.

I feel Rhonda's hands on my spine, releasing knotted cords of tension and am transported back to the present moment. To Cat/Cow Pose and her Saturday Beginners' Class. I'm not a beginner, but my choices have forced me to start over.

I don't have a vinyasa in me right now. I cannot bring myself to flow.

"Unfurl your spines," Rhonda instructs us. "Imagine you're a cat, recoiling in fear, yet, also, paradoxically, terrified of nothing. You have nine lives to live. Nine incredible, immense, expansive lives, and, despite that, you fear. The word *fear* stands for 'false evidence appearing real.' Release the lie of your anxiety as you open your heart in Cow Pose."

I open my heart and feel more, rather than less, afraid. Rhonda seems to intuit this somehow because she places a reassuring hand on the small of my back. I accept her compassion, do as I'm told, drop my forearms, lift my hips, and allow my teacher to adjust me, to anchor my body into place, to massage my weary hamstrings. My ankle-brace mocks me, but it is soon forgotten as I walk my feet toward my forearms, then gracelessly maneuver from my cockamamie modified Dog into a legit Forward Fold.

"Really? All those grapes?" April asked at the grocery store. I'd put a bag of green, a bag of purple, and a bag of red, into my cart. Three bags of grapes for a single, lonely person.

"I like grapes," I told her.

I eat them like popcorn—in front of the TV—because I can't use, and they keep me occupied. I crunch them, chew them, eviscerate each tiny orb, one at a time. Nibbling has become my substitute for smoking joints and doing lines. I used to roll the most skillfully crafted blunts. Now, I arrange my grapes by color and pop them in my mouth one by one.

I took a green grape from the bunch, popped it in my mouth, and chewed.

April surveyed the contents of my cart. "What are you planning to *eat?*"

In addition to grapes, I'd filled the wheeled green mesh food-conveyance vehicle with butter, peanut butter, bottled water (which I take with me to yoga), carrots, celery, rice cakes, granola, coffee, half and half, and Jell-O.

"I dunno," I replied. "Eggs, sandwiches, microwave dinners..."

"But you don't have eggs, or meat, or bread, or cheese," she pointed out. "And I don't see any microwave dinners."

"I forgot."

April sent me away to get some actual food. I returned with eggs and nothing else. She sent me away again. I came back—this time immediately—because I couldn't remember what I was supposed to retrieve. There's a word in AA which describes a specific type of temporary wet-brain where a person can't form coherent thoughts: *mochus.*

I peered into my shopping cart again and scratched my empty head.

April sighed. "Wait here." My sponsor used the same tone she reserves for her kids when they're being simultaneously adorable and exasperating. A few minutes later, she returned with a can of tuna, a jar of mayonnaise, some bread, half a pound of deli turkey and half a dozen Smart Ones TV dinners. "This okay?"

I nodded. I didn't tell her I don't own a can opener. April had been infinitely patient with me and my inept mind all morning, and I didn't want to exhaust her seemingly-endless supply of patience.

In the checkout line, I handed my PA Access card to the cashier. She looked at it, then looked at me. I hung my head. That card is my Scarlet Letter. Girls who look like me aren't supposed to need food stamps.

Rhonda puts her hands on the nape of my neck and gently massages.

"Let's transition," she says. "Remember: Breath is the connective tissue between postures."

I know I need to move beyond the limited space of this Forward Fold, but being here feels so good that every part of me recoils at the idea of something else. Especially when that something is unknown.

I wait, anxiously, for her instruction.

15

I'd hoped the physical complexity of Lotus Pose would distract me from my racing thoughts. No luck. I've contorted my legs into a pretzel, and, still, every time I close my eyes and try to focus on my body, all I find is another memory.

"Dude, there's a zebra in the bathtub."

It's February 28th—my birthday. And, because my friend Jed's parents are out of town, he's invited nearly a hundred people to their Main Line mansion in honor of my nineteen years on earth. I've never seen a zebra up close before, let alone one with the audacity to crash a party, then spend the whole time hanging out in Jed's claw-footed antique bathtub. There's gum in my hair—a huge wad of it. I'm not sure how it got there, but I've ducked into the bathroom to untangle my blonde strands from the gooey, chewy Watermelon Wave bubiliciousness.

My attempts aren't working. I've been at it a while. I peer into the mirror at the wadded pink clump. Is it possible it's even worse? Wait! What's that? Reflected in the glass is the outline of an unfamiliar shape behind the green plastic curtain.

I pull the shower curtain back.

"Holy shit!"

I don't mean to be rude. I don't want to offend the zebra. But the last thing I'm expecting is to find a striped horse in a bathtub.

This one has bright eyes, a purple tail, and an attitude. "Girl," he says, "you look like hell."

He doesn't. He looks spectacular. And exotic. Instead of the usual black, this zebra's stripes are the colors of an iridescent rainbow.

While I agree with his assessment (My hair looks torn up), finding a talking equinesque animal in Jed's bathtub is almost as exciting as if I'd discovered Lady Gaga chillin' in the outdoor Jacuzzi.

"Wait here!"

I run back out into the party and grab the arm of the first person I see.

"Dude! There's a zebra in the bathtub!"

The person attached to the arm looks at me with an expression as noncommittal as his or her gender. What is with this whole emo culture? Or am I just so high I'm oblivious to what should be obvious?

"You're as high as a kite," he/she says.

I insist that the androgynous partygoer come with me to look at the bathtub.

"Fine," he/she says. "But you are being totally insane right now."

"Look," I say, "I know what I saw. I'm not crazy and I'm not making it up. You'll see..."

Only, when we get there, instead of a zebra, we find Jed in the bathtub. He's overdosed on the same batch of drugs he and I had shared earlier.

I open my eyes and realize that I'm crying.

My legs are still twisted. Only, now, instead of sitting upright, I've slumped forward over them.

I undo my Lotus, but, because my joints ache too badly to get up immediately, I remain sprawled out on the floor waiting for the soreness to dissipate. It was premature to attempt such a complicated pose. Lotus used to be easy. Not anymore.

It's 10:03 Sunday morning and the day stretches ahead of me—another interminable twenty-four.

Mom's probably in church right now, Dwight at home, a Sam Adams in one hand, the remote in the other.

I rub my aching legs, scramble to my feet, and proceed to do the only thing I can think of that won't intensify my pain.

"Hey. Everything okay?" April isn't expecting to hear from me. We talked an hour ago, after I woke up, sweating, from a using dream and called her in a panic.

She told me to take a shower, eat some breakfast, and try to reorient myself in the present moment. "You're sober," she reminded me. "Two months now, right?"

"Fifty-three days."

"Right. Using dreams will happen. They still sometimes happen to me, and I've got fifteen years now."

While I was fucking strangers and buying crack, the chronometer of April's abstinence had notched past the fifteen-year mark.

"And what do you do about it?"

"I pray. I meditate. I go to meetings. I do all the things I do any other day. And I tell Howie and the girls I love them a few more times than usual because remembering where I used to be makes me grateful for where I am."

I'm not grateful. I'm wistful.

So, even though I've intruded on my sponsor's life once today already, I humble myself enough to reach out again and admit the extent of my neediness. It was either call her or Markus.

"I feel tangled up," I tell April. "And I'm not sure what to do about it."

Before she can reply, I anticipate her answer. Yet, hearing her advice feels like loving, adjusting hands, bringing me deeper into a posture. "Go to a meeting."

I need to kill some time, so I walk to the eleven o'clock Sunday Morning God of Our Understanding Meeting at the West Mount Airy Rec Center. Nevertheless, I—an agnostic at a meeting about God—arrive almost forty minutes early.

The doors are locked. I find a rickety bench out front, take a seat, and will away the intrusion of memories of how I used to spend my Sundays, and of a faith that no longer works for me.

A man, his son, sacrifice, sins, an apple eaten, a woman condemned, a cross borne, pain before a resurrection...

I know I'm supposed to have a Higher Power, but believing in God strikes me as akin to having an imaginary friend. If I were still on talking terms with Mom, I'd ask her how and why she believes. We haven't spoken since she called me on my birthday and I picked up, drunk, singing the Happy Birthday song to myself.

Dwight was with her.

"Hi Jessica," Mom said.

"Hi Jesse," he added after her.

"Happy birthday," they said together.

"Another year older," I slurred. "How's that for a fucking gift?"

"Hello!" A woman approaches, smiling broadly and holding an AA *Big Book*.

"Hi."

"Looks like someone else got here early too. I can let us in." She dangles a glistening key in front of me. A shiny object, like a talisman or an antique pocket watch. Just that quickly, the past recedes and I no longer feel a need to obliterate the present.

As usual, April's suggestion was helpful. I'll follow this stranger into an anonymous room and, once everyone else arrives, we'll sit in a lopsided circle and share deeply of ourselves. After an hour's over, I'll make the short trek home, eat at least three handfuls of grapes, then find a coffee shop to sit at with my *Big Book* and journal and while away the day until dinner and a second meeting—the only nightcap I currently allow myself, and a bookend to keep the spine of my sobriety riveted in place.

⸗ 16 ⸗

Funny. I used to hate serving coffee to snarky suburbanites, and, now, I'd give anything to have to remake the same Espressino for the third time because my definition of a "light dusting" of cocoa powder is *obviously* inadequate. Anything for my paltry paycheck and all the free bagels I can eat. Anything to get out of my head.

April and I are sitting at a corner table at the Free Café, splitting a spinach-stuffed croissant and talking about the steps. It's the last Friday in September and Erika and Annabelle are at school so I have my sponsor's undivided attention until 2:30, when she has to leave to pick them up.

"I don't understand," I say again. "How is saying I have no power and pretending to believe in some bullshit deity supposed to make me a better person?"

April sighs. No matter how many times she's explained the steps to me, I'm still as clueless as ever. I'm not trying to be dense, but this stuff doesn't make sense.

The first step is to acknowledge you're an asshole and can't be trusted not to screw up your life. In the next two, you give up all responsibility and let some unknown external force take over. Step four delves into the specific ways in which you're a fuck-wad. Then, in step five, you have to confess these ways to someone whose job it is to love you while acknowledging that you have, in fact, been an asshole. Steps six and seven are all about continuing to own your assholery and humbling yourself while—once again—avoiding personal responsibility so some external force can "change" you. Then, in steps eight and nine, you demoralize yourself even more by going to the people you wronged, apologizing, admitting the full extent of your assholiness, and attempting to make it right. The last three steps involve doing your best to avoid any additional lapses into schmuckdom while, at the same time, helping some other shithead who is just coming to the realization that he (or she) is an asshole—like you used to be, and still often are.

I'm on step one.

"What happened to your hand?" April gestures at my gauze-covered fingers. Luckily, I still had gauze left over from my post-hospital wrist-mummification days.

"I cut it."

She studies my face.

"By accident," I clarify.

Last night, I tried to open a can of tuna without a can opener. I hacked at the lid with a knife until I finally got one jagged edge to lift. Then, as I attempted to pry the remaining part up, I gouged myself. A bloodbath ensued. In the end, I threw the red-soaked tuna away, washed my slashed finger in the sink, wincing as the water licked my wound, then ordered greasy Chinese takeout, which I had to eat one-handed.

I make a mental note to buy a can opener.

"It looks vicious."

"It was." I suck the spinach from my teeth and run my tongue along the empty crevices.

"So, tell me about your powerlessness," my sponsor instructs. "About the ways your life is unmanageable."

What is there to tell? I can't even manage a can of tuna.

"What do you want to know?"

"Do you finally understand that you're an addict, and that you'll never be able to drink or use in moderation?"

I take a bite of croissant and chew.

I understand. I just don't want to.

"I know I am." I point to my head. "But..." I touch my heart. "I don't feel like I am."

"What more evidence do you need?"

"I dunno."

"You think that, if I handed you a beer and laid out a line of coke, you could stop at one beer and one line?"

"No."

"Even if I offered you a million dollars?"

I shrug. "Probably not."

"So, you admit you have a problem?"

"Yeah. Definitely."

"But you don't accept it?"

"I'm not sure I understand the difference."

She launches into a fifteen minute explanation about how we can't change anything until we accept it. I try to focus, but April's words swim inside my skull, as slippery as the fish I used to try to catch with Daddy at our house at the shore. I was the only one who'd ever go out in the boat with him. Mom and Chloe hated fishing, but I liked anything that involved being at his side.

April keeps talking well past my capacity to understand, or internalize. “Jess?”

I don’t say anything. I simply take one last bite of my savory, flaky, spinachy deliciousness and chew until the whole thing falls apart.

17

Everyone does a collective eye roll.

None of us move.

Rhonda surveys the room. "C'mon," she coaxes. "Frog Pose isn't *that* bad."

We obey. Reluctantly.

The beer-bellied fifty-something man on the mat next to me mumbles something under his breath. The woman on the other side of him lets out the softest, barely discernable "shit" I've ever heard. With my knees bent, my butt up in the air, and my forearms on the ground, I feel like a yoga piñata, ready to be busted open.

Then, Rhonda says something profound. "Notice your resistance. Sometimes, we can learn more about ourselves when we're opposed to something than when we easily accept it."

As I lie—belly-down, ass-up, like an idiot—I realize that Frog Pose is my step one. I'm powerless over my inability to do it perfectly. Yet, here I am, forced to submit.

Rhonda approaches. "Beautiful Frog Pose."

My teacher can't see my resistance. She sees only my willingness and pliability. I relax my pelvis and breathe until the barriers in my mind and body melt away and I feel a deep inner opening.

Today is the twenty-seventh anniversary of Daddy's death. I usually try not to remember—to push down the grief that, even after all these years, refuses to subside. But I do. Today. Always.

I thought about texting Chloe or Mom. Only, I wasn't sure what to say.

Congratulations on your aliveness.

Happy deathaversary.

Do you blame me as much as I blame myself?

Instead, I did what I've become good at—distraction.

I cleaned my apartment while listening to Macklemore on replay, watched all three *Godfather* movies, one after the other, then came here—to yoga—where I'm forced to slow down enough to experience something beyond the superficial.

Slowing down, as hard as it is, offers both a way in and a way out of pain. I let the sensation in my pelvis—exquisite in its anguish—hurt in a way that is at once tolerable and true. If only I didn't run from so much, life would be easier.

"Okay," Rhonda says. "You've suffered enough. Take Baddha Konasana and let yourself relax."

Who knew? Suffering—seemingly intolerable—can be alleviated when I am willing to accept, rather than resist.

When class is over, I sprint out of the studio. So much for relaxation and restoration. I arrive, breathless, at my car, switch my iPhone on, and scroll through my recent calls. This breakthrough feels too important not to share.

April answers on the second ring. "Hey Jess, you okay?"

"I'm powerless." I huff and puff into the phone. "I'm powerless, and my life has become unmanageable."

By the time we hang up, my whole body feels alive with newfound realization. I thought accepting powerlessness would feel spirit-crushing. But *this*... *This* isn't what I expected. I sit in my car, trembling with energy that demands to be expelled.

"I'm powerless!" I yell. "I'm really fucking powerless! Aaaaaaannnnnddddd my life is unnnnnnnnnmanaaaaaageeeeeeable!"

With the windows up and the doors locked, I scream until my car vibrates and my ears reverberate. Then, I turn my key in the ignition and head to a meeting.

≈ 18 ≈

I expect the Friday Night Young People's Meeting at the Manayunk Clubhouse to be full of college kids and court-mandated high school dropouts. But, at thirty-two, I fit right in.

April has been encouraging me to start going to more meetings on my own.

"It'll help you to meet new people and make some friends. You don't want to only go to the meetings I go to. Besides, you might want to complain about me sometimes."

"I complain about you all the time," I remind her.

She laughs. "I mean behind my back."

Meetings without my sponsor are a bad idea. Or, rather, they're a phenomenal idea, but an inept execution.

Trey is forty-four—a decade too old for a Young People's meeting, and by far the oldest one in the room. He is twelve years sober to my two months and four days abstinent. When the meeting ends, he weaves his way through the crowd.

"Hi," he says as soon as we are face-to-face. "I liked your share."

Trey isn't my type—despite my thing for older guys. He's slender and straight-laced and a little too polite. Still, it feels good to be wanted by someone who isn't wanted by the cops.

"I forget what I shared about."

He doesn't realize I'm not joking. "Good one. Jess, right?"

"Yeah."

"What meetings do you go to?"

I rattle off my schedule with the rapid-fire precision of the militantly newly sober. Monday this and Tuesday that and Wednesday... My routine is as predictable as it once was erratic. I'm learning that it has to be, if I'm ever going to get the hang of living life without substances.

"Cool," Trey says. "Hope to see you around."

Suddenly, Trey is everywhere—at the Monday night Beginner's Meeting, the Tuesday Recovery from Relapse, the Wednesday morning God of Our Understanding. We lock eyes across dusty church basements and butterflies flutter in my stomach. Before meetings, he sidles up beside me and asks if the seat next to me is taken... If he can buy me a free cup of AA coffee... How my sobriety is going... Through his shares, I learn that this older man is a deeply-sarcastic, marathon-running, music-aficionado who works for the Coast Guard and commutes to Virginia three days a week and is home, in Philly, the rest of the time.

"Why do you commute when there's a base in Philadelphia?" I ask him.

"I didn't always. I used to be stationed here, but, a couple years ago, I got a promotion and that meant working out of Arlington."

"Why wouldn't you just move there?"

He smiles. Wipes a wisp of wayward hair out of my face. "I like all that Philly has to offer."

After meetings, Trey and I run into each other—on purpose by accident—at Pablo's Pizza, or the Ridge Avenue Diner, or the coffee shop down the street where we AAers congregate for better beverages than the bitter swill we force down while listening to one another's stories and spilling our own secrets.

"I didn't know you were coming out," Trey always says, prompting me to wonder how little-white-lies fit into the framework of his supposedly honest sobriety.

It's from Trey that I first hear "Those who do not recover are people who cannot or will not completely give themselves to this simple program, usually men and women who are constitutionally incapable of being honest with themselves." He reads the words at a *Big Book* meeting, then shares about how disclosure has been an essential part of his sobriety.

"I didn't know you were coming either," I reply.

We try not to be too obvious about sitting side-by-side amidst our twelve step fellows or how intent we are on squeezing the last dregs of conversational pulp out of each interaction, but we're always the last to leave, the ones most reluctant to say goodbye.

I'm not sure what Trey sees in me, although I know what interests me about him. I've finally met a man who has his act together, whose bills are paid, who isn't about to start drinking, and who shows up when he says he will. Because of his commuting schedule, I'll see Trey four nights in a row, then we have a built-in three-day break. I don't mind the breaks. I'm still early enough in sobriety that I need a lot of me time to mope around and watch endless hours of TV, cry at the slightest provocation, and burrow under the covers and wallow in unmitigated misery. Daily interactions would be too much for me.

After several mock-dates in group settings, Trey and I find ourselves alone in the parking lot when he casually mentions his love of the Delaware shore. "It's beyond beautiful."

"Really? I've never been. My family always went to Jersey."
He smiles. "We'll have to rectify that."

19

I feel guilty for lying to April. Last night, when she asked what I was doing today, and if I wanted to come over and help her and the girls decorate the house for Halloween, I said I'd made plans to hang out with a girl from AA.

"Really? Who?"

"Someone I met at the Young People's Meeting." I've learned that, when lying, it's best to stay as close to the truth as possible.

Telling April about Trey would mean opening my choices up to scrutiny, and I'm not in the mood for some sponsorly lecture.

"Okay. Well, if you feel like trick-or-treating on Wednesday night, Howie and I are taking Erika and Annabelle out around six."

"Cool. Thanks. I'll let you know."

On the Saturday before Allhallows Eve, Trey picks me up in front of my apartment in a sleek black Mazda—the kind of car that inspires confidence and isn't in need of a jump or a new transmission. I slide in beside him.

"Hey. You look great." As he reaches for the stick shift, Trey's hand brushes against mine. Tiny skin pricks of sensation travel up my spine. "Cold? I can adjust the temperature."

He's got the A/C on full-blast even though it's October.

"Thanks, but I'm cool."

"No pun intended."

It's not funny. We laugh anyway.

"I know it's weird," Trey acknowledges. "But one of the things I started doing when I first got sober was making my car and my apartment cold all the time."

"Why?"

"It reminds me not to get too comfortable, or complacent."

"I get that." I think about my fridge full of grapes and fraying yoga mat. We all have our strategies for keeping demons at bay.

An hour later, Trey finds a spot directly in front of Captain Ahab's—a quaint seafood eatery with a view of the Delaware shore.

"This is the place."

The restaurant's exterior is painted to look like the body of a whale and has an ivory-fanged doorway.

"Looks great."

I unbuckle my seatbelt and start to open my door, but Trey says, "Let me."

As I watch him walk around the car and do something I could've easily done myself, I try to be grateful, instead of impatient.

"After you."

With Trey's hand on the small of my back, I lead our procession of two into the yawning mouth of Ahab's whale. Inside, there are tiny pictures of cartoon whales on the covers of the menus and the entire wait staff is wearing captains' hats. We're four couples back in the maître d' line, and, when it's our turn to request a table, the Captain of Cod tells us it'll be a thirty-minute wait. "I'll put your name on the list," he says. "Until then, you're free to sit at the bar or walk around."

"Walk!" Trey and I are unanimous in our desire not to be up close and personal with all that top-shelf alcohol.

"This is nice." Trey clutches my nervous hand in his slightly sweaty grasp as we stroll down the Delaware sidewalk.

"Yeah," I agree. "It's fun getting to know you."

In AA, dating happens in reverse. Instead of starting out with our accomplishments and letting the skeletons out of our closets over time, we begin by divulging the messiest parts of our lives. Trey tells me about living in Seattle and dating the ex-girlfriend of a gun-runner, how one of his former lovers tried to run him over with her car, and getting fired from sixteen jobs in a single year.

"I was a different person when I was drinking," he explains.

I don't tell him that, drunk or sober, I'm the same—hooking up with guys and lying about it to the women who love me. I do tell him about my endless string of relapses, the two times I almost died, and what growing up without a dad was like.

Because AA has taught us both to refrain from taking another person's inventory (out loud), we don't ask a lot of questions, or issue any judgments, or try to one-up each other with stories of our own. We simply listen.

As we make our way back to the restaurant, Trey consults his watch. "It's been twenty-five minutes. We should probably see if our table is ready."

"Wait." I point to the eclectic knick-knack shop a few doors down from Ahab's that I somehow failed to notice on our stroll out, but which, now that we're crunched for time, seems to be calling to me. "Can we? Just for a second...?"

In answer, Trey opens the door. I step past him, surprised, once again, by his chivalry. The last few guys I've been with never held anything for me, except a bong and that was always more of a mutual puff, puff, give arrangement.

"Are you a big shopper, Jess?"

"No." Since leaving Mom and Dwight's, I've been too cash-poor for anything other than essentials.

That's not true. Anything that didn't *feel* essential.

The basket of mood rings on the counter beckons. "The last time I saw one of these was in the movie *My Girl*. I used to love that movie."

Trey hands the cashier a couple of bucks, then hands me one of the kaleidoscope rings.

I put it on. It stays black.

"I think this one's defective."

The second and third rings remain black too. Trey puts a fourth one on his own finger. It turns a brilliant shade of blue. I shove this final ring in my pocket and pretend I don't care about having just been declared empty by some retro pieces of costume jewelry.

"Let's eat," I say. "I'm starving."

Over dinner, my date and I laugh about the disparity in our ages—and in our lengths of sobriety.

"You're most definitely robbing the cradle," I tell him.

"Or I'm thirteenth stepping you..."

"Or both."

Trey takes a bite of his chicken. I savor my swordfish. We leave the restaurant technically sober, but drunk on each other.

"This was great," he says as we climb into his car. He thinks it's over.

"So... What's your place like?"

"It's a loft in East Falls."

"I like lofts." I couldn't care less about architecture.

"Wanna see it?"

Despite the very adult renovated factory, cutting-edge architectural style, Trey's unit is reminiscent of a college dormitory. Upstairs, he's constructed a makeshift desk out of a couple of milk crates and a slender sheet of plywood. Atop the budget work-structure are a sticker-festooned laptop (Evidently, it's imperative to pay tribute to Nirvana, Kiss, and the Grateful Dead while looking up Internet porn on one's MacBook) and too many CDs to count. Downstairs is where Trey keeps his wall-to-wall collection of records, framed nerd-culture posters, and still-in-the-box action-figures. His kitchen is devoid of everything except bottled water and Ramen noodle soup.

"Are you sure you're forty-four?"

I feel like I'm back in high school, hooking up with one of the seniors whose parents were chill enough to give him the entire basement as a bedroom. But Trey's laugh lines and sun damaged skin confirm that he is, indeed, approaching middle age.

"Where do you sleep?"

He points to a well-worn futon.

I sit on his bed/couch and smile. "It's more comfortable than it looks."

As if he doesn't know. As if I'm not sitting in the exact spot where he closes his eyes and invites himself to dream.

"It's cold in here."

"Should I turn up the heat?"

"It's okay. I'll warm up." I burrow beneath Trey's comforter.

When he joins me, his body is tight and taut from daily twelve-mile runs. As he presses himself into me, I open my lids ever so slightly and take in his translucent skin in the dim light of the dark room. He's like the Glo Worms of my youth. Like the one I called Glinda and never let Chloe play with after Daddy died. I kept that luminescent maggot far past what was appropriate because he'd given it to me, then got rid of it at fifteen. After what I'd done, I couldn't look her in the eyes.

I shimmy off the futon, sink to my knees, and take Trey's firm, straight, pulsating penis in my mouth.

Shit. It's even colder now that I'm half-naked.

"Jess..."

"Yeah?"

I'm making a mistake. Trey's a nice guy. I like his bitterness, his stories about crazy ex-girlfriends, his quick-witted criticisms and snappy one-liners. But *like* is going to be the most I can ever muster. Besides, I'm early in my recovery and he's far into his.

"You're beautiful."

I'm Eve—not worth the temptation. Yet, I do what another older man once taught me to do and lick, suck and bob on the forbidden fruit of his loins until Trey is ripe with desire. Then, I climb on top and pump my body up and down until we come together—an illusion of a connection that doesn't actually exist.

"That was..."

"Yeah."

"You were..."

"So were you."

"Want to spend the night?"

"I shouldn't. I've gotta be up early for Sunday morning yoga and the God of Our Understanding Meeting."

"Right. I'm planning to go to that too, so I'll see you there."

"Right."

I force myself to let Trey hold me for an hour before driving me home where I can crawl into bed warm and alone. When I wake, his scent still on me, I don't feel bad, exactly. Just... empty.

I miss Halloween with April, Howie, and the girls. Instead, Trey comes to my place where I never get trick-or-treaters because no one in the building has kids and we watch *Seven*—or half of it anyway before becoming occupied with other activities. He doesn't sleep over. Being sober has made me less willing to spend more than a few hours at a time with a man. It's too vulnerable and intimate. I'm not ready for that kind of closeness. That's probably why, if I were brave enough to talk to April about it, she'd tell me that early sobriety isn't a good time to be dating.

Screw that. Early sobriety isn't a good time to be alone.

Trey and I see each other for two more weeks before having *the talk*. We do it before the Tuesday night Recovery from Relapse Meeting, mostly so I'll have a place to dump my disappointment afterward and not end up drinking over it.

We each have a viable, convenient excuse for calling it quits. I think he's a great guy, I tell him, but I'm too early in my recovery to get tangled up in a relationship. He tells me he doesn't feel right about robbing me of my time for personal growth.

"I can leave," Trey offers, after we've swapped rationales. "I don't have to stay or share or anything. I'll catch a meeting tomorrow. It's more important for you to be here."

But I'm fine.

"This is my first grown-up break-up," I admit as we sit outside the meeting, ending what's only just begun.

He laughs. He doesn't realize that I'm not bullshitting.

There's no drama. No tears. No hurling objects at heads. No overdoses.

We allotted fifteen minutes for the conversation, but it's over in less than five.

"You sure you're okay?"

I nod. I've never felt more normal in my life.

"Want me to go?"

I shake my head. "We're good, Trey. Really. No reason we can't be at the same meetings."

He holds the door. I walk in. For the first time since we met, we retreat to separate corners instead of intentionally unintentionally sitting together.

"Hey Jess!" A girl I recognize whose name I don't know because she rarely shares and I'm self-centered greets me with a smile.

"Hey."

"How are you?"

"I'm... neutral."

Shouldn't I be feeling something? Disappointment? Remorse? Relief? If breaking up doesn't even hurt a little, Trey and I were right to end it.

"How are you?"

It isn't until halfway through the meeting that I realize that it does hurt. Not the breaking up, but the fact that I'm alone. Sober and alone.

20

"What the fuck is *that*?"

April nudges me. "You can't say fuck in a yoga studio."

I laugh. "*You* just did."

I point, again, at the photograph of the scantily clad woman in an inverted pretzel. "Seriously, what do you even call that?"

"Um… impossible?"

The woman is supporting her entire body weight with her hands—like a handstand—but her legs are contorted into Lotus.

"Um… exhibitionism?" I counter.

The figure in the image is wearing a jog bra and the kind of butt-coverage-only shorts that high school cheerleaders put on under their skirts to keep from flashing people during their *Rah Rah Sis Boom Bah*s.

I've been coming to Serenity for sixty-six days and I've never seen this obnoxiously reverential photo before. April either. Sometimes, on Saturdays, I bring her with me to Rhonda's Beginners' Class then, afterward, we go for scones and she listens to me vent about my problems.

A door opens. Rhonda emerges. She has tears in her eyes, but, at the sight of my sponsor and me, wipes them away with the back of her sleeve. "Hi Jess. April."

From behind our teacher steps the woman from the image—as stark and surreal in life as in the glass frame on the wall.

Rhonda gestures at the apparition. "Meet Kama."

Kama is dressed entirely in Lululemon and has shocking crimson hair, which she's separated into pigtails. I hate her immediately.

"Karma?"

"Kama." Her voice is heavy with enlightened condescension. "You know… the Sanskrit word for desire."

"Oh, of *course*."

She's a redheaded Goddess—an anorexic Aphrodite.

"Ka-ma." April sounds out the word as if she's a kindergartener. "Are you a teacher?"

"We are all teachers and students simultaneously." Her non-answer is so patronizing it makes me want to slug her.

Rhonda rolls her eyes. "Kama is the new owner of the studio."

"Congratulations," April says.

I don't say anything. I'm too self-centered.

"C'mon," April pushes me toward the studio door. "Class is starting."

"Will this new ownership impact us?" I whisper.

"Change is life's only constant," she whispers back. "Now shut up, so I can practice."

I take a seat on my mat and attempt to whitewash my mind. It doesn't work. In the silent space of stillness, a wave of terror rises up from deep within and crashes on my shores, capsizing my illusions. In Fish Pose, my throat open, my once infant soft-spot pressing into the hardness beneath me, I finally confront the reality that I'll never be able to get high again and drown in the loneliness of letting go.

"Wasn't that great?" April asks as soon as class is over. "I feel so invigorated."

I feel as wrung out as a sponge. "Were we even in the same class?"

The other students filter past, but I hang back to thank Rhonda for helping me arrive at yet another breakthrough. Only, when I glance inside the vacated room, I see my teacher alone on a mat, saluting the sun, engaged in her own practice, her own process. I'm not about to interrupt her to talk about me, and it's clear she doesn't need to talk about herself. No matter why she was crying earlier, Rhonda will be okay. Yoga, not I, will offer her solace. She is teaching, by example, how to flow through feelings.

I turn and walk, silently away.

21

November eighteenth. I'm at the Free Café with a notebook and free cup of coffee, courtesy of Tina.

"I like just can't like wait for you to come back to work," she said when I walked up to the counter, my backpack slung over my shoulder, and told her I was stopping in to read and write.

Some days, being in my apartment, alone with my thoughts, is too much to handle—especially when I'm supposed to be working on the steps. So, here I am, pen in hand, coffee growing colder by the second, trying to come up with something greater than myself, and greater than drugs and alcohol, that I can turn to.

My mind is blank.

I write *yoga* at the top of the page, then cross it out.

I did yoga hung over. I did yoga high. I flowed through posture after posture, while convincing myself that I was striving for enlightenment, then left class and snorted lines of coke.

As for God, I outgrew Him somewhere between the day Daddy died and the night I first sucked Dwight's cock.

I look at my step-journal.

Step two: Came to believe that a power greater than ourselves could restore us to sanity.

April has instructed me to make a list of all of the Higher Powers I can think of. "Be open," she told me. "You don't have to *believe* in anything right now. You just have to come up with possibilities."

Being open is harder than it sounds for someone as closed-minded as me. But my sponsor bested me with the words of Herbert Spencer: *There is a principle which is a bar against all information, which is proof against all arguments and which cannot fail to keep a man in everlasting ignorance—that principle is contempt prior to investigation.*

So, here I am, reluctantly willing.

I write:

1. God
2. Yahweh
3. Buddha
4. Nature
5. The twelve-step group

6. Universal energy
7. Science
8. Freedom
9. Angels
10. Goddesses
11. Mermaids
12. Unicorns
13. Yoga
14. The interconnectedness of the human spirit
15. Breath
16. Focused intention
17. Morality
18. Love

Even with the list, I feel as empty as ever. Emptier, actually.

What's wrong with me that I can't put my faith in *anything*?

I pick up my phone and step outside into the cold.

"There is no God," I say, as soon as April answers. "Pretending feels pointless."

"Are you sure there's no God?"

"Yeah."

"Sure enough to bet your sobriety—and your life—on it?"

There's a long pause. Something about the way my sponsor asks the question is a noose around my neck, cutting off my capacity to answer.

"Google *Pascal's Wager*." She hangs up before I have a chance to reply.

Thirty seconds later, back inside and scrolling through the internet on my IPhone, I find what I'm looking for. Leave it to April to cite seventeenth century French philosophy. Even though I'm skeptical, I'm also pragmatic. And Pascal's argument makes sense. I'm still not about to believe in a heaven and hell after this life, but I can easily believe in hell on earth. I've been there. I'm pretty sure my sponsor is telling me, in her gentle, unassuming way, that, if I don't find a Higher Power, I'm doomed to go back to the fire and brimstone of addiction.

Another look at my list and I'm confronted with the limits of my faith. It's ironic. I was more "spiritual" when I was using.

One time, I saw Jesus weeping on a subway and gave him a pilfered Whole Foods napkin, which he used to wipe away his tears. A few months after that, we ran into each other again, at a concert, and, even though the Messiah didn't remember me, that didn't keep us from getting stoned and screwing in my friend Isaac's van. Actually, we didn't fully consummate our connection. Jesus had floppy beer dick and couldn't get it up—or in. That's why I can't add him to my Higher Power list. He's probably mad at me anyway. He called half a dozen times after that concert, and I never once called him back.

Pre-conversion Mary Magdalene seems cool. The woman at the well too. I wonder whose list of sins is longer, hers or mine...

This would be easier if I had Mom's faith, but I can't do Catholicism. Not after three years of fucking her husband after church on Sundays.

Dwight and I didn't *only* do it on Sundays. We did it whenever the opportunity presented itself. But Mom and Chloe always stayed at church—Mom for the second service, Chloe for youth group—and Dwight always took me home early for our own brand of worship.

I skim through the AA *Big Book*, review my list again, and add *My Creator* to the list. I cross it out though. How can my Higher Power be *my Creator*? My Creator—the woman who gave birth to me—wasn't even paying attention to what was happening under her own roof.

"I missed you while you were gone. Is everything okay?"

I look up and Jimmy is peering down at me—concern etched into his smile.

Evidently, falling off a roof changes how you see things. In the four and a half months since I last saw him, my former admirer's face seems to have become less pockmarked, and his eyes aren't nearly as beady. I stuff my *Big Book* in my backpack, but leave my journal on the table. It's a gold-embossed notebook from Barnes & Noble with no characteristics that marks me out as an alcoholic.

Even though I've chosen to do my step work here, that doesn't mean I want Jimmy or Tina or anyone else knowing the real reason for my absence. Sure, my life used to be a train wreck, and I didn't try very hard to hide it, but, if I tell them about my newfound sobriety and relapse—again—then I'll be a failure, rather than a fuck-up.

Luckily, Tina is too self-involved to notice anything but her nails. Today, they're the same shade of yellow as my pee whenever I try to be healthy and take too many vitamins.

"Everything is great," I tell Jimmy. "I'm almost done recuperating and I'll be back behind the counter soon."

"Talk about bad luck. First mono, then falling off a roof."

I study the Formica tabletop, trying to muster the words for an apology, but, when I look up, three new customers have entered the café. Their bodies at his back force Jimmy forward to the counter where he gives Tina his standard order, and, while his attention is averted, I slip out without saying goodbye.

22

It's eighteen days before the official start of winter, twenty-one weeks after my fall off the roof rendered me temporarily disabled, and here I am reporting for my first official day back behind the counter at the Free Café. My boss is paying me under-the-table because I'm still not cleared to go back to work.

"Let's see how you do before throwing you back into the full swing of things," he suggested.

If all goes well, when I go to my GP next week, he'll approve me for part-time employment. Then, I'll send in the required paperwork and have the disability payouts adjusted accordingly.

When I told April the old me would've stayed on disability as long as possible, even after going back to work, she said, "Congratulations. You're not a user anymore—of people or of substances."

It's after the morning rush and before those in need of their afternoon caffeine pick-me-ups arrive en masse for frappe-latte-mocha whatevers. Tina is in the bathroom shellacking her nails, and I've got my back to the door while I grind a new batch of beans in the anticipation of the customers to come.

"Ahem."

I spin around. Jimmy is back. This time, the place is empty and it's just the two of us.

My cheeks burn. I was stupid to slink out without so much as a "see you later."

"Thanks for what you said the other day. Sorry I didn't stick around to talk. I just –"

"I get it. It got busy. Anyway, I shouldn't have interrupted. You looked like you were doing something important."

"Jimmy, you're important. I'm sorry for being such a shit to you."

He shrugs.

Without him having to ask, I anticipate his order and hand him a cappuccino in a to-go container. "Hey… It's slow as hell today. How about I treat you to a scone or something and we hang out?"

"Like a date?"

I shake my head. "I'm still not interested in you that way, but I'd like it if we could be friends."

Jimmy considers my offer. "I'm not a huge fan of scones. How about a chocolate chip muffin?"

"I can do a split!" I run into work, ecstatic after yoga, and practically collide with Tina.

Between my first day back and this one, the doctor cleared me to return for real at the coffee shop. But only part-time. He said it was "better to ease in than to overdo it and risk a setback."

I didn't ask if he was referring to an addiction recovery setback or a physical rehabilitation one. And I didn't argue. I'm getting better at trusting the people I rely on to know what's good for me. Working again—even in a reduced capacity—is great. It gives me more to do than yoga, meetings, stress-eating, and watching obsessive amounts of *Law & Order*.

Not that I'm needed today. The Free Café has been deserted all week. Tina and I have scoured every surface, rearranged every display, and played *I Spy* so many times we're both "like totally like bored."

She looks at me over her neon orange nails and grins. "You cannot."

"I can."

"Let's see."

I didn't have to come in until two today, so I went to the Friday Morning Stretching For Strength class that Kama recently added to the Serenity schedule. She taught it herself and, although I still can't stand her, it was a nice change from the Hatha and Beginners Flow classes I've been sticking with out of fear of resuming anything that reminds me of the me I used to be.

Prior to the roof incident, splits were never a big deal. Aggressive, full-contact, Sati-style yoga turned me into a ganjaed-out Gumby. But my body still isn't back to where it was before the accident. With Kama's encouragement, for the first time in what feels like forever, I slipped into a full Hanumanasana.

"Like, like totally!" I exclaim.

Tina is unaware that I'm mocking her. "Awesome."

I slip off my shoes and head behind the counter in my jeans and sock-clad feet. "Watch this." I put my right foot in front of my left, and begin to drop down into a split. Only, socks on linoleum don't ease. The floor is so slippery, it sends my right foot on a crash course forward. Behind it, my left leg buckles.

These jeans are too tight. I shouldn't have tried this out of spandex. Is it possible to die of a split-related injury?

As I hurtle toward the ground, I hear a sharp tearing sound as I enter—gracelessly—into the most painful split of my life. "Fuck!"

"You o-o-o-k-k-k-ay?" Tina is laughing too hard to be helpful. "That like l-l-l-o-o-o-ks like it like r-r-r-e-e-e-a-a-a-lly hurt."

"You think?" I want to be mad, but I'm laughing too as I collapse into a fetal position, rub my groin, and bite back tears. As I lie on the floor, clutching my crotch, I can't help but wonder if, maybe, there's a lesson in this. I tried to force something, and, now, I've hurt myself. There's no way I'll be able to even attempt a split again for weeks.

Tina stops examining her fingers long enough to stare down at my grimacing face. "Seriously, Jess, that looked painful. Do you like need me to call an ambulance?"

"No." I shake my head. "But can you get me some ice for my vag?"

23

When I get to the dilapidated old church at the corner of Sprague and Sedgwick Streets, and sprint down the stairs to the dingy basement, the room is already aglow with candlelight. A circle of chairs has been set up and flickering embers illuminate all the different faces—some old, some young, some pudgy, others gaunt. These are the faces that haunt me when I get a sudden urge to use. The faces that offer embers in the darkness of my mind.

The Monday Night Eleventh Step Meditation Meeting is the AA equivalent of a restorative yoga class. As I glance around at the sober silhouettes, I feel as if, in this moment anyway, we are stronger than the sum of our addictions. Then, just as quickly, recognition slams into me—as if I weren't looking where I was going and crashed straight into a wall.

Oliver.

Failed condoms and early ejaculation.

He waves. I pretend not to see him and skulk into the shadows.

"Welcome to the Monday Night Eleventh Step Meditation Meeting. I can't think of a better way to spend our New Year's Eve than right here—sober and serene." The meeting leader rescues me from the awkwardness of any possible pre-Preamble, ex-fuck-buddy small talk.

I settle into a metal folding chair and close my eyes—partly to shut out the images that surface at the sight of Oliver's smile, but mostly so I can listen to the Saint Francis prayer and let its words sink in.

"Lord, make me an instrument of thy peace!

That where there is hatred, I may bring love.

That where there is wrong, I may bring the spirit of forgiveness.

That where there is discord, I may bring harmony.

That where there is error, I may bring truth.

That where there is doubt, I may bring faith.

That where there is despair, I may bring hope.

That where there are shadows, I may bring light.

That where there is sadness, I may bring joy.

Lord, grant that I may seek rather to comfort, than to be comforted.

To understand, than to be understood.

To love, than to be loved.

For it is by self-forgetting that one finds.

It is by forgiving that one is forgiven.

It is by dying that one awakens to Eternal Life."

I might not give two shits about religiosity or dogma, but the prayer revives a longing in me that I thought only yoga had the power to activate. The first person I ever heard recite the Franciscan friar's words was Mom on the day of Daddy's funeral.

She'd been too destabilized to come up with any words of her own, so she'd settled on a simple recitation that I didn't fully understand at the time, although I grasped its overall meaning: Let go of selfishness and find salvation—a credo I'd fail miserably to live up to.

"Now, sit in quiet contemplation for ten minutes." The leader sets a timer.

Twenty heads and forty eyes go down as people meditate and pray and clear their minds of extraneous thoughts. I use my minutes to visualize the words *peace, love* and *light* painted on my heart—a technique I learned a long time ago from a spiritual guru I met in an Arizona ashram after a bad break-up sent me searching for answers.

Rama and I smoked Ayahuasca, practiced rain-dancing, and told ourselves we were enlightened. Then, she got arrested for indecent exposure (Apparently, rain-dancing is fine; *naked* rain-dancing not so much) and I headed east again to the life I knew and hated. But, before we parted ways, Rama taught me how to see a word written inside my body, focus on its image, and breathe.

I see the words *peace, love* and *light* and imagine that they are bright enough to dispel the darkness within.

The first time I tried to kill myself was in the front yard of a three-bedroom, split-level in Ardmore. I was eighteen and had just let myself into my boyfriend's parents' basement and found him in bed with someone else. The pain of his betrayal was enough to make me slit my wrists.

Wait. That's a lie. Anthony and I hated each other.

Most of our relationship was spent fucking and getting high and hurling objects and obscenities at each other. Once, I blasted him on the side of the head with my shoe. Another time, he whipped a glass vase at me. It hit me in the small of my back, fell to the floor, and shattered. We were forever stepping on fragments of broken glass.

I never would've killed myself over him.

I'd been wanting to die for a while. Walking into Anthony's makeshift apartment and finding him in bed with a pair of ginormous tits attached to a heavily made-up brunette was nothing more than a convenient excuse. I hurled a pillow at my boyfriend's head, grabbed a razor out of his bathroom, then ran—screaming—past days' old congealed Chinese food and stale, half-smoked cigarettes into the cold December night.

Outside, the air was fragrant. Pine-scented. The kind of air that precedes stocking stuffing, tree decorating, and baking cookies for Santa. Yet, the streets felt desolate as I huffed my way through one, then two, then three sprinted blocks before I collapsed, breathless, in the snow.

From a nearby yard, a snowman leered. He was missing a nose and had no hat or scarf to protect him against the elements, but that didn't stop him from condemning me with his hard, charcoal eyes. Who was *he* to judge *me*? I hated that snowman and the people who'd made him. Fuck them and their stupid Christmas. I couldn't stand their multicolored lights, or the wreath on their front stoop. Through the open drapes, an imposing pine mocked me with its lifetime of accumulated ornaments.

Daddy used to let me place the angel atop our tree. He'd hoist my tiny body in the air and we'd pretend that I was flying. I loved setting the white-clad, winged woman on her perch and knowing she'd be watching over us. Loved taking her down too. Even then, I had a knack for dismantling things.

Through the window, I can see the stranger's tree topper: a shining plastic star.

Stupid star. Stupid ornaments. Stupid family. For Christmas, I'd give them the gift of a dead body on their lawn—my open veins spilling red across their pristine white snow.

I cut—deep, jagged gouges with my now ex-boyfriend's stolen razorblade—and let my blood drip onto their yard. Then, because I couldn't bear a witness, I kicked the snowman until he sunk to his slushy knees.

"Screw you!" I screamed just before cutting again.

A deeper incision. More blood. Cold permeated bone. This time, the blood didn't drip. It drowned.

I slumped beside the snowman and waited for death's inevitable release. Only, the family—a man and wife and their two little girls—came home and rescued me.

I was lying at the ruined snowman's feet, so didn't see the father park his minivan, or sprint toward me. But I felt his strong arms as he scooped me up.

"Katie, quick, throw me a blanket!"

His voice was loud. I wished he would be quieter. I was tired and wanted to be left alone.

The wife, Katie, did as she was told, then ushered her girls inside. Guess she didn't want them to see my combat boots and too-short skirt and tight white tank-top, my nipples erect from the cold—death's pin-up girl, bloody and sexy and twisted.

There was a tearing sound as some other girls' dad ripped his daughter's baby blanket, then pressure as he tied scraps of cloth love around my wounded wrists. The doctors told me later that those poorly-made tourniquets saved my life.

When they were safe, Katie came outside, cellphone in hand, talking to a 9-1-1 dispatcher. "Come quick. This poor girl's life depends on it." Then, the wife and mother of two sat beside me and whispered reassurances into my frostbitten ears. "Have faith," she told me. "You'll be okay."

But I couldn't believe in anything that didn't come in a bottle or a baggie.

Apparently, as I passed out, I said exactly four words because later, at the hospital, the doctors asked me about them.

"Who's Dwight?"

"My stepdad. Why?"

"The couple who saved your life said you said, 'I love you, Dwight.' That's really nice that you're so close to your stepdad."

I started crying. I hadn't cried before. They thought it was because I was happy to be alive. That's what I let them believe, so they'd release me—after a twenty-four-hour psych observation—secure in the belief that I was no longer a danger to myself.

The timer dings. I take a deep breath. Open my eyes. Around me, the others are surfacing, too, emerging from their own inner experiences into the reality of this basement and the shared struggle that binds us together. I raise my hand. It's time to admit that my leap off the roof, my drugged descent, wasn't an accident.

≠ 24 ≠

Light streams through my window and slaps me in the face. This sucks. I just managed to fall asleep a few hours ago. Ever since last night's meeting, the realization of what I've twice tried to do has been gnawing at me. After it was over, instead of sticking around and talking to people, which would've helped, I bolted. I told myself I was avoiding Oliver, but, really, I just couldn't be around people to whom I'd admitted the depth of my self-hatred. So, I went home and watched the ball drop and thought about how another year is starting and I'm still as much of a disappointment as ever.

I slink out from beneath the sheets, walk to the window, and peer outside. Dawn should be beautiful. Expansive. This dawn is bleak. Nothing is happening. The streets are as empty as my life.

It's as if I'm the only person in the entire city of Philadelphia who's awake right now.

I unroll my yoga mat, then roll it up again. Yoga would be useless. There's no breathing through this sensation. No inviting some "Higher Power" into this space. This is a desperation that goes too deep for a few Sun Salutations and a couple of Pigeon Poses. I throw on a pair of jeans and my rattiest sweatshirt, corral my un-brushed, unwashed hair into a haphazard ponytail and give my teeth a half-assed scrub. Even my dealer deserves better than morning breath.

It's early, but Markus caters to teachers, doctors, school nurses, janitors, cafeteria workers, soccer moms, and stockbrokers. People who get up early because there are people who depend on them—even on New Year's Day. People who don't take off from their responsibilities.

Not me. The Free Café is closed today and April, Howie, and the girls are going to New York City to see the Rockettes at Radio City. I have nowhere to be and no one who needs me. I can step out of life. I've earned it. Besides, it isn't just New Year's. It's also the five-month anniversary of my sobriety.

I can't believe it's been more than five months since I last saw Markus. He used to call me Blondie and tell me I was his "favorite customer." As nicknames went, I liked Blondie. Not as much as Jesse though. Daddy was the first to call me that. Mom hated it. She said it sounded like a boy's name, but he told her he thought it sounded tough.

"She's got a fighter's spirit," he said. "Besides, Jesse is a great name. Think about all the famous Jesses in history—Haines, Tannehill, Burkett and *both* Renos."

"They're all dead."

"Alright, fine. How about Helms?"

"They're all men. I don't care what you say, Walter, I'm not calling her anything but Jessica. A beautiful name for our beautiful girl."

"She can be beautiful *and* strong."

Later, when she tucked me in, Mom kissed my forehead, her long blonde Rapunzel braid hanging down in my face, thick and sturdy, and pulled myself up into the tower of her love.

"Goodnight, Mommy."

"Jessica, did you know that your name means 'God is watching?'"

I shook my sleepy head.

"Well, He is. Goodnight my beautiful girl. Sweet dreams."

Mom and Dad were both wrong about me. I'm not beautiful, and the fight went out of me a long time ago.

I trudge out into the falling snow. Just that quickly, the sky opened up. Whatever light there was is gone.

"Why bother staying sober if this is all there is?" I say to no one.

The sky hurls snowflakes at my head. By the time I climb in my car, my hair has slipped free of its inadequate ponytail and is plastered to my cheeks. My shirt is soaked. I slam the steering wheel with my fist.

"What's the fucking point?"

Step two is a joke. Sobriety isn't worth it. Higher Powers don't exist.

I start the car.

A hit will make this better. Just one hit. Anything to take the edge off—coke, pot, Adderall, acid...

A sudden image of Warrior I—the strength of armies contained in a 90-degree knee-bend, forward hips and elevated arms—flashes in front of the windshield. I wipe it away.

As I drive through the violent onslaught, my thoughts are riveted on escaping the inner chasm I've been trying to fill for twenty-seven years.

If I called April, I know what she'd say. "Getting high isn't the answer."

But I can't call April. She, Howie, and the girls are on the way to the station to board a train to New York City for brunch and a kick-line matinee. And I can't deal with the monotony of sobriety anymore. It's boring. Predictable. Pointless.

The roads are slick and I'm going too fast. Wet, wilted leaves destroy any possibility of traction. I should slow down, but, when I take my foot off the accelerator and apply it to the brakes, my attempt to decelerate sends me spinning. The car fishtails. I pump the brakes. Nothing. The Hyundai spirals. I hit the brakes again and turn the wheel. My attempts are useless, so I do the only thing I can—steel myself for the inevitable impact.

Only, there isn't one.

When I open my eyes, my car is stopped on the side of the road. I'm alive. Unhurt. Shaken, but okay. I get out. The Hyundai looks the same as always. I haven't hit anything, but I have been hit with a realization. Something—or someone—doesn't want me getting high today.

I feel silly and melodramatic, yet I drop to my knees on the snowy side of the road and offer up the first real prayer of my adult life.

"God, I still hate you. But, if you love me, please keep me sober."

⸗ 25 ⸗

"You're a fucking cunt!"

I stare blankly at him.

"You *liked* me!" He is in my face—invading my personal space, breathing on me with minty-fresh rage.

Can he really be this angry because I don't want to fuck him again?

"Who told you that?" I ask.

"We had *sex*, Jessica." Garrett towers above me, his arm outstretched, pressing on the concrete behind me.

"We did. What's your point?"

He hisses something unintelligible.

"Just let it go, okay?"

"What did I do wrong?" Now, Garrett's tone is more plaintive-puppy than Pit-bull.

"Listen, it's not you." I stop myself from offering up the second half of the cliché. "I have too much going on to complicate my life. I just wanna stay sober."

"I'm not getting in the way of your sobriety."

"Right now, you are. I'm trying to get into the meeting, and you're blocking me."

Garrett has me cornered. My back is against the wall.

The snow is dingy now, gray and dog-piss yellow—instead of white and untouched.

"Jessica, I like you."

"You just called me a fucking cunt." My jacket is insufficient protection against the cold.

"I was angry. I'm sorry."

"You're forgiven."

Is he seriously leaning in to kiss me?

"I think you're really special, Jess." More mint.

I turn my face to keep his lips from landing. "You don't even know me."

"How can you say that?"

"Because I don't even know myself." I take a deep breath. Sharp winter air assails my nostrils. "Listen, Garrett, my sponsor says no dating for a year." April hasn't actually said anything about dating, but it sounds like something a sponsor might say, and I remember a woman sharing in a meeting once that her sponsor had forbidden her from dating until she reached a sober year.

The word is magic. *Sponsor.*

Garrett steps aside and lets me pass. "I'm sorry. I had no idea."

Neither did I. I make a mental note to use this trick again.

"My sponsor says..." I'll say, and people will respect what follows.

Evidently, what *I* say doesn't matter. Some things never change—even with sobriety.

Inside, the temperature is warmer. I slip out of my coat, settle into a chair in the back of the room, and remember another time I tried to invoke the power of no.

It didn't work.

"Come on. You know you want it."

I didn't know his name—could barely focus on his face. With all I'd had to drink, my vision was a split-screen—two strangers, as opposed to one.

"You're hurting me," I tell him.

"Take this."

I do as I'm told. The pill goes down easy. He waits until I dissociate. That way, I don't have to feel what comes next. I can pretend what we're doing is consensual.

When he finishes, I take another hit. Do another line.

I wake and the stranger is gone, and with him all traces of holiday cheer.

I head for the shower where I try, unsuccessfully, to wash away the memories.

I'd gone to McMenamin's hoping to escape the loneliness of another solo Christmas Eve, and he'd stopped in for a drink, after buying presents for his wife and kids. I had no one to buy presents for. Sure, there were Mom and Chloe and Dwight, but we weren't on speaking terms since I'd gone over to the house for a barbeque, went outside to smoke a joint, and accidentally set fire to the gazebo.

"You look lonely." The stranger smiled wryly.

"You look married," I replied.

A ring of glistening gold—as expensive as I was cheap.

"So what if I am?"

"So what if *I* am?"

"You don't have to be lonely tonight—if you don't want to be."

"You don't have to be married..."

He slipped the ring off his finger. Put it in his pocket.

I took him home. I wanted to have sex—would never have protested if not for the pain—yet, when he started to insert himself into my exit place, I told him to stop. As uninhibited as I pretended to be, there were certain things I reserved for people I loved.

But the stranger handed me that purple pill and sent me to a place where nothing hurt and everything was permissible.

"My wife won't do anal," he complained, after it was over. "She's a prude."

My sympathy was as stretched as my sphincter. "I'm not your therapist," I snapped. Then, gentler, "Forget about her. Forget about everything. That's what I'm doing."

I wasn't. Not really. I was still lonely. He was still married. Nothing could obliterate those facts.

Water scalded my flesh. The timer on my watch alerted me to the fact that it was, officially, Christmas.

It's the most wonderful time of the year
There'll be much mistltoeing
And hearts will be glowing
When loved ones are near
It's the most wonderful time of the year...

Except that, for me, it was just one of many nights a man I didn't love or like, or even know—a man whose face I wouldn't recognize in the daylight—had been inside me.

I thought about hating myself for fucking someone else's husband. Only, as husbands went, this one wasn't a big deal. After Dwight, anyone else was innocuous by comparison.

Besides, I already hated myself.

Garrett is at the coffee pot—avoiding making eye-contact—as April hurries in and settles into the empty seat beside me.

"You didn't want to get farther away?" Before I can reply, she hands me a Let it Snow t-shirt. "Happy New Year, Jess."

I'll add it to the Lululemon sweatpants she gave me for Christmas. My only gift, other than a check from Mom and Dwight's joint account—both their names on the top left corner, only one in perfectly-penned script on the signature line at the bottom right.

Evangeline Carrington.

A card this year, but no call. After my drunken birthday self-serenade, I can't say I blame them. Still, I'm five months sober now. Stable enough to be invited for a holiday, or granted the civility of a voice-to-voice hello.

26

"Hi. I'm Carla. You have a beautiful practice." The diminutive Asian woman smiles at me as she unrolls her yoga mat.

I've seen her in class before but haven't introduced myself. Without the conversational lubricant of alcohol, I've become weirdly shy and uncertain. Plus, she intimidates me. Her poses are so precise, her breathing so unobtrusive. She's a purebred straight from the groomer. I'm a stray mutt.

"I'm Jessica."

We shake hands.

"Don't you love Rhonda's classes?"

I nod. I've graduated to Rhonda's Sunday afternoon All-Levels Vinyasa. Still not as intense as the classes I once took, but challenging enough to keep my mind engaged and my body pliable.

"I've had a lot of different teachers, and there's something truly special about her."

"I know."

"It's like..." she continues "... like all her teaching stems from her soul."

It's such a profound thing to say. I wish I were profound.

I have nothing to add, so I change the subject. "So, Carla, what's your deal?" It's a stupid, artless, socially inept, question. No wonder I have no friends outside of AA.

Carla chortles. "My *deal*?"

She must think I'm an idiot, but it's too late now to pretend I'm normal.

"Yeah." I try to play off my asinine first question with equally awkward follow-ups. "What makes you tick? What are you passionate about? What's guaranteed to make you cry? You know... your deal."

Carla opens her mouth to speak, then bites back her words as the studio door swings wide and more students flood in. Rhonda plugs her IPod into the speaker portal and soft, somnolent sounds wrap themselves around us. The last student filters in, the latch clicking into place behind her.

"To be continued..." my mat-neighbor whispers.

For the first time, I look around the room—*really* look, expanding my scope of focus beyond my own rubber rectangle. There's the man whose leg twitches with anxiety, the flaxen-haired woman with the sparkly engagement ring, the harried young mother whose darkly-circled eyes bespeak of sleepless nights and early mornings, and the light-skinned African American man, his dreadlocks a tribute to his ancestral heritage. I've been mat-to-mat with these people for *months*, yet I know nothing about them. I haven't bothered to go deeper than snap-judgments and surface impressions.

What, I wonder, do they think of me? They probably assume the blonde with the ever-changing eyes that shift from blue to gray to green, depending on the weather and her mood, is either recovering from an eating disorder or clinical depression. I cry a lot and keep to myself and, since the accident, my once cavernous chest and protruding bones have been obscured by flesh and fat and muscle.

The class has ebbed and flowed and ebbed again. I struggle to catch up. Luckily, in Rhonda's classes, there is no catching up. She tells us that, even if we feel lost and out of synch, we're always exactly where we're supposed to be.

When class is over, as we roll up our mats, Carla resumes the conversation right where we left off. "My deal is that, six weeks ago, my husband told me he's gay. I come to yoga partly to get out of the house and partly to cultivate my intuition. I mean, how could I have been *living* with a man for the past four years without having any idea that he's gay?"

I open my arms. She steps inside. We are two fractured people, coming to our mats in search of salvation from our respective desperations, bonded together by the pain that is this life.

"Want to grab a cup of coffee?" Carla suggests. "Tell me your deal too..."

"I can't tonight," I reply. "I have plans. But next week? Either before or after class?"

We make a date.

By the time I get to my car, my lips are so stretched from smiling that my jaw hurts. It's been a long time since I've met anyone new (outside of the people in AA). Maybe, I'm finally developing a life. Not much of a life, but a life.

Step Three:

Made a decision to turn our will and our lives over to the care of God *as we understood Him*. (Happy Baby Pose)

27

"I won't!" I scream.

I'm five-years-old.

"C'mon, Jessica," Mommy coaxes.

"No!" I run upstairs and hide my face beneath my Little Mermaid covers.

Mommy knocks, softly, on the door. She doesn't understand that I can't see him. I won't. As long as I refuse to say goodbye, he can't die.

Only, that isn't how it happens. A week after I storm into my bedroom at the house we've always lived in as a family of four, I stand beside Daddy's casket, sobbing into Mommy's pretty black dress. She doesn't scold me for ruining the fabric. She simply holds me close.

I want to crawl into his grave, I tell her, so I can say I'm sorry and make him wake up.

"That's not how it works."

"How does it work?" I want to know.

"It'll be okay." Her mouth says, but her eyes tell me she's lying.

Chloe stares at us, her lips curved into a question mark. My sister isn't even two yet. She doesn't understand our tears. At the service, she sits, fidgeting on the pew beside me, while Mommy reads aloud the words of a man so good the church says he was shot straight to heaven in a cannon.

It is by self-forgetting that one finds.

"What should we do now?" Mommy asks after everyone has left and we're back at the house with the roof that betrayed us.

I look around. Mommy, Chloe, and I are surrounded by casseroles, flowers that have no scent, and frames full of images of the man we just watched descend into the ground.

"We can do anything you decide," she says.

"Let's get Daddy back."

She explains that that's not what she meant. She wants to know if I want to rent a movie, or go to the park, or play dress-up. Those things—she tells me—I have the power to decide. Life and death are up to God.

I push away the memory of the first time I felt truly powerless and look again at the words of step three: *Made a decision to turn our will and our lives over to the care of God as we understood Him.*

Unlike the house I grew up in, my apartment has no pictures in frames or on the walls—no desire to memorialize the past. Every Bible Mom's ever given me is rotting in a landfill. She may have found solace in the God she taught me to believe in, but the man in the sky has only ever let me down.

I prayed every night, out-loud and in my head. I begged and pleaded and wished and hoped. I told myself God was just playing a practical joke. The God I knew and loved would never let it be true that Daddy was gone *forever*. For months, I remained unwavering in my conviction that, at some point, the big man in the sky would reveal the sleight of hand, deliver the necessary punch line, and return Daddy to me. Then, Mommy met Rodney—the man she dated for half a decade before she met Dwight. After that, I stopped praying. After that, I realized Daddy wasn't ever coming back.

Rodney was cruel. I've come to appreciate that about him. He never pretended to love us, never lulled us into a false sense of safety, never gave us hope that he could act as a replacement for the man we'd lost. Dwight wasn't like Rodney. When Mom first brought him home, I actually thought *We can be a family again.*

Mom's new husband became my Higher Power. I believed in him. Until I didn't.

I look at my step-journal again.

AA pretties-up the language—softens it around the edges. Tells me I can choose a God "of my own understanding" to turn my will and life over to. But the God of my childhood took my dad from me and let me fall in love with the only person on earth who should've been off-limits.

"Where the fuck were you?" I shout at the ceiling. "I needed you and you weren't there! Why should I trust you now?"

No answer. Only silence.

28

"Do you smoke?"

Coffee isn't working. I'm as exhausted and irritable as I was when I woke up this morning. Probably even more so. I've been sitting at this quaint Mt. Airy café, less than a mile from my apartment, reading and re-reading the same paragraph half a dozen times because I couldn't concentrate at my place and thought this would be a better atmosphere in which to read my *Big Book* and chill out for a while.

I'm most definitely not chill. I dog-ear the page I'm on—not that it matters (I'll have to start over anyway, when my brain isn't so jumpy)—and thud the book closed.

The man grinning down at me sports a well-maintained goatee and—despite the fact that it's *morning*—a five o'clock shadow. His vibe is sort of OCD meets grunge. His jeans are ripped too symmetrically for their tears to be accidental. And his t-shirt is stonewashed, rather than burnout. Plus, he's wearing Birkenstocks which scream *EXPENSIVE!* and *HIPPIE!* and *ASSHOLE!* Birkenstocks on a Saturday in January. And we're *outside*.

Espresso's owners have erected a three-sided tent so that people can come, even in the coldest months, and enjoy a hot beverage out of doors. There are at least a half dozen portable space heaters, and the outdoor fire pit makes it fairly toasty, but Birkenstocks are just plain obnoxious. This schmuck clearly grew up affluent, and, despite his best efforts to seem cool and unassuming, it's clear from the way he's dressed, and his cocksure confidence, that he's a poser.

I glare up at him. "Smoke what?"

He laughs. "Mind if I do?"

"Mind if you what?"

He thinks I'm flirting. I'm not. I'm done with men. Bathroom men and barroom men and backseat men, and all the others. They hurt too much.

The stranger lights a clove cigarette and takes a drag. "My one vice..."

Because the tent isn't fully enclosed (It's missing a wall), the vapor tendrils away into the atmosphere.

I peer down at my book. Anything not to make eye-contact.

"How about you?"

"How about me *what*?"

"Vices. Have any?"

"Many. Cigarettes are not among them." I open the book.

The waitress comes outside and asks if I'd like more coffee. I tell her I do, and she hurries back from where she came. Poor kid. When I came in, I couldn't help but notice that the place was understaffed. There's only two people working today and the other patrons—who have wisely opted to sit indoors—are so closely clustered together that if I'd opened my *Big Book* in there, the other patrons could've read every word, including the footnotes.

"So, you're staying for a while?"

"Planning on it."

Goatee guy takes this as an invitation to sit in the empty seat across from me. "I'm Paul."

He sticks out his hand. I let it hang in the air between us, like someone's lost birthday balloon. He looks at me, deflated.

"That's nice," I say.

I hate the name Paul. It reminds me of the apostle.

"And you are?"

"Not interested." My tone is about as warm as a gas station slushy.

"Aw, c'mon." Paul smiles. "I'm not a jerk. Promise. I just see a pretty girl sitting by herself, staring at the AA Bible, and feel duty-bound to talk to her."

"If it's the AA Bible, isn't talking about it a form of sacrilege?"

He laughs.

"Why don't you go talk to her?" I point to the only other person on the terrace—an elderly woman in a puffy down jacket and pink pussy hat. Guess she didn't get the memo that they've suddenly become offensive. She's reading the *Chestnut Hill Local* and sipping tea. The carpet bag by her feet is overflowing with skeins of yarn. Knitting needles peer over the top of it.

"I will."

Paul walks over to the slumped-shouldered, geriatric stranger and introduces himself.

A slow, creeping smile overtakes the woman's broad, wrinkly face. She gestures to the chair opposite her. He sits. I don't wait for my second cup of coffee, or tell the waitress I'm leaving, or say goodbye to the scruffy-faced smoker. I certainly don't wait around to see what he'll do next. I simply gather my belongings, leave a five dollar bill on the table and slip away unnoticed.

There's no room in my life for Pauls right now—apostolic or otherwise.

≠ 29 ≠

Carla and I look ridiculous standing in line at Starbucks with our yoga mat bags slung over our shoulders like bindles. She's wearing a mock Japanese kimono dress over a skin-tight yoga outfit which fits her tiny frame like OJ Simpson's glove, which is to say it's too tight. I'm in head-to-toe Old Navy because I can't afford Lululemon.

We order lattés and Carla gets herself a Rice Krispie treat.

"I'm emotionally eating," she informs me. "I've gained at least seven pounds."

"Understandable," I reply.

"My husband has a boyfriend."

"Boyfriends are overrated."

She takes an angry bite of her snap-crackle-pop and marshmallow solace.

"Don't worry," I assure her. "He'll get his heart handed to him, and you'll have your revenge."

"I draw the line at hearing them have sex. I've told Tim that, if he brings his boyfriend home, I will cut his dick off while he's sleeping."

"No jury on earth would convict you."

"Exactly."

"Just to clarify... The boyfriend's dick or your husband's?"

"Does it matter?"

I contemplate the question. "Guess not." Blow on my latté. "What about you, Carla? Are you seeing anyone?"

"You mean besides Johnny Depp in my fantasies or the pizza delivery guy who comes to my place at least once a week? Nope. Not a soul."

"Why not?"

"Because, believe it or not, I'm still in love with Tim. I know we're over, yet I can't let go. My brain screams 'Move on, you're an idiot!' and my heart says 'Hang on, there's still hope.'"

I nod.

"And you?" Carla takes a sip of her drink. "You dating?"

I take a sip. Good. Not too hot. "No."

"So, Jess, what's your *deal*?"

I take a deep breath. Even in the midst of my most destructive escapades, I've never admitted my *deal* to anyone outside of AA. But I've gotta start somewhere, and Carla's been so open with me...

"I'm an addict and alcoholic," I admit. "This past summer, I got shitfaced, jumped off a building, and almost died. I started coming to Rhonda's classes as a way to stay sober."

Carla's smile is a sip of water on a scalding summer day.

I take the morsel of proffered Rice Krispie treat from her outstretched hand.

"You know, Jess, I think we've both hit bottom and are trying our best to get up again."

I wipe away a tear. I hadn't realized how heavy a secret could be—until now.

"Can I do anything?" she asks.

"You are doing something. By not judging me."

"You know what we need?"

I wipe away another grateful tear. "No. What?"

"Some Rhonda yoga."

When Carla and I arrive at Serenity, Rhonda's bright yellow VW bug isn't in the parking lot.

"She's usually here by now."

"Weird," Carla agrees. "But we're a little early."

I check my watch. Class starts in five minutes. "Not that early."

When we walk in, Kama is sitting behind the desk smiling her big guru smile.

"Hello ladies." Bright white incisors and pointy canines.

"Where's Rhonda?" Carla demands.

"Rhonda?" The studio owner seems surprised by the question. Nevertheless, she expands her smile all the way to her molars before issuing her reply. "She's no longer teaching here."

"What happened?" I can't imagine Rhonda would leave without warning us.

"Oh, you know..." Kama waves one of her long arms. Her bracelets jangle like wind chimes on a breezy afternoon. "Yoga is about nonattachment. All is impermanent. I'm sure you'll enjoy my class though. I don't bite. Promise."

What does bite is the fact that Rhonda is gone and I didn't get a chance to say goodbye.

I look from Kama's bright red hair and condescending smile to her image, captured behind glass. I've been to this studio so many times. Yet, until now, I've never noticed the slow, creeping crack in the bottom of the frame. I have a sudden urge to thrust my fist through the transparency, remove the photograph, and tear it into yoga confetti.

Instead, I decide to let my feelings out on the mat.

That's what Rhonda would do.

That's what she did.

I think back to the day I saw my teacher crying and made the choice not to ask her what was wrong and make a mental note to add her to my fourth step, when the time comes.

"Should we stay?" Carla whispers as we set up our mats. "We could protest."

I shake my head. I need my asana fix. Especially now.

"This bitch had better bring it," she hisses.

As if on cue, Kama sweeps into the room with her Pippi Longstocking braids. "Let us breathe."

Namaste bitch. Anyone as sexy as she is shouldn't be sporting a kindergartener's hairstyle.

I sit on my yoga mat and trace the loop of my breath until something shifts.

My exhalation is a child's permission slip, hastily signed, granting consent for the little girl inside me to explore her sadness. The tears feel bigger than my body can contain. I open my eyes, but, when I look around, I see that Carla's shoulders are shaking too. And I realize we're each crying about much more than Rhonda. I watch her ribcage expand as I feel mine do the same—our syncopated breathing signifying something or nothing, depending on my willingness to accept that we are united in our grief and, yet, somehow, alone with it too.

I reach out a quivering hand, interlace my new friend's fingers with mine, and squeeze. She squeezes back.

We both keep crying.

≠ 30 ≠

I don't know why April insisted I come tonight. I can barely breathe, this meeting is so overcrowded. Too many bodies stuffed into a ground-floor conference room, but, because of the weather, no one wants to open a window.

I should've gone to yoga. I can always breathe in yoga.

Jenny, the teacher Kama hired to replace Rhonda, is teaching a one and a half hour restorative class tonight. Most of Serenity's other classes are only an hour long, and I crave those extra thirty minutes like I used to crave cocaine.

Still, sobriety first. Besides, I like speaker meetings. They offer a chance to delve more deeply into someone's story than a typical three-minute share. Plus, it's helpful to hear about another person's evolution. It makes me believe positive transformation might be possible for me too.

April has been telling me all week that the guy they got to tell his story is going to be inspiring. She knew him before he got sober, and she says he used to be a chronic relapser—like me.

"If he can get sober," she said, "there's hope for us all."

I take my seat beside my sponsor.

"I'm glad you came," she says. "You'll never guess what Annabelle did today."

Annabelle is April's youngest.

"What?"

"She asked me how babies are made."

"She did?"

"At six. Can you believe it? They grow up too fast."

"What did you tell her?"

"The truth."

My mother wasn't capable of telling me the truth. How could she be when she didn't know it?

I'm too old for *the talk*. I've already had *the sex*. Nevertheless, Mom has decided to sit me down and lecture me about the birds and the bees.

Dwight looks as uncomfortable as I feel. "Do I really have to be here for this?" he asks—again.

Mom gives him her we've-already-discussed-this look, the same look she uses whenever I ask to stay out past curfew. "Jessica, I'm sure that, by now, you've heard about sex in the classroom. You've probably even heard some things from your peers."

Dwight rolls his eyes. Last night, while Mom and Chloe were out Christmas shopping, we fucked six different ways: woman on top, doggy style, reverse cowgirl, standing up, spooning, and, of course, missionary. Over and over, my stepdad and I bumped our respective junk until we came all over his and Mom's William Sonoma sheets.

He washed them after. I still haven't learned how to use the washing machine.

"Intercourse and all that goes with it can be confusing," she continues. "If you're anything like I was at your age, I'm sure you have a lot of questions, and Dwight and I decided we'd rather you get your answers from us than your peers or teachers or, worse yet, TV."

Dwight smirks. "Yup. Your *mom* and I decided."

Mom mistakes her husband's sarcasm for sentiment and squeezes his hand.

He takes a sip of coffee to conceal the upturn of his lips. "Do you have any questions?"

I turn toward my mother. "Yeah. Why is *he* here?"

"Because he's your father. Well, not technically. But he's a father figure, and you can trust him. I wish my own father had talked to me about this stuff."

I sigh.

"Really, Jessica, better you hear about sex from us than from some testosterone-driven teenage boy."

"Okay." I lean back in my chair and fold my arms across my chest. "What's a blow job?"

Dwight spits out his coffee.

Mom blushes. "Well," she says, after taking a moment to compose herself, "it's when a woman inserts a man's erect... um... member into her oral cavity."

"When a girl sucks a guy's dick," Dwight clarifies.

Mom shoots him a sideways glance.

"What?" he says. "Your explanation was confusing. An 'erect member'?"

I slap my forehead. This is so dumb there are no words to describe how dumb this is.

Dwight knows I know what a BJ is. I give them to him all the time. He's just throwing Mom the proverbial bone (or, in this case, boner). Not me. I refuse to play along. The last thing I want is to sit across the kitchen table from the woman whose husband I'm fucking and talk about sex.

"So, Mom, do you give Dwight blow jobs?"

Her coffee cup trembles. Liquid sloshes over its side.

"And how often do the two of you fuck?"

More sloshing coffee. Dwight looks down at the table. The sides of his face are rose-red, but I'm not sure if that's from embarrassment or anger.

I go further. "Or, should I say 'make love'?"

"Our sex life is none of your business," Mom snaps. "If and when you're ready to discuss the subject like an adult, I'll be ready to talk to you about it. Until then, *Jessica*, I've had enough of your nonsense." She storms out, leaving me alone with her husband.

As it turns out, it wasn't embarrassment or anger. Dwight grins. "You've got balls, kid. Never let anyone tell you different."

"How often *do* you two do it?"

He shrugs. "Not that often."

I nod, take a sip of coffee, and return his smile. "Good."

I don't care that they still have sex—as long as it's not all the time. I'm seeing a couple other guys myself.

Dwight and I have an open relationship. It works better that way.

Frank, the meeting leader, checks his watch and clears his throat.

"Oh." April squeezes my arm. "The meeting is about to start. I'll tell you about Annabelle later."

In tandem, we turn away from each other toward the front of the room. I know I know the guy sitting next to Frank from somewhere, but I can't place him. He recognizes me too, because he gives me a hello head nod. I hope I never made out with him at a party, or got high with him, or, worse yet, drank too much and threw-up on his shoes.

Whoever he is, April's already told me he used to be a regular here, until he went away to treatment in Connecticut. Evidently, he moved back not too long ago, and, according to the AA grapevine, his story is amazing. Now that I think about it, that explains the atypically large Thursday night crowd.

I picture everyone here with pom poms and megaphones. Gimme an S, s, you got your s, you got your s. Gimme an O, o, you got your o, you got your o... What's that spell? Sobriety!

After Frank reads the Preamble, the pseudo-stranger introduces himself. "Hi. My name's Paul and I'm an alcoholic."

Paul. I stare at his scraggly facial hair, sharp eyes, and broad smile.

That's how the coffee shop smoker knew about the *Big Book*. What did he call it? The AA Bible... I was right not to be nice to him. He's got the kind of lethal smile that could mess up my sobriety.

"I'm really glad to be here tonight to talk about my experience of the third step. When Frank asked me, I said, 'You sure you want me to talk about step *three*? I'm much better at powerlessness and unmanageability than surrender.' But Frank pointed out that the best stories involve struggle, and I struggled a *lot* before I became willing to make the decision to turn my will and my life over to the care of a Higher Power."

Paul pauses to survey the crowd.

"I'm thirty-five. I've been sober for a little over two years now. But, between the ages of fifteen and thirty-three, my life was a shit-show."

"He's not lying!" Frank interjects.

A few people chuckle.

Paul grins, then continues. "I was a shy kid. I kept to myself and didn't have a lot of friends. Then, I found alcohol. It took away my shyness. Unfortunately, it also took away my motivation, and plunged me into depression. I quit sports, stopped studying, barely went to class..."

Sounds a lot like me, although I was never shy.

"I graduated high school with a 1.8 GPA and only got into college because my SAT scores were decent and both my parents are professors. I spent my college years smoking pot, hooking up, and getting wasted. Then, one night, during my sophomore year, I got blackout drunk at a party, got behind the wheel of my best friend's car, and drove us headfirst into a tree. I walked away. Danny didn't. He lost a leg and suffered a severe brain aneurism. My parents hired a lawyer and, somehow, I got off with parole and expulsion from the college."

He exhales. Inhales. Opens and closes his fingers, forming fists. Is he angry at himself? At alcoholism? Maybe, like me, he's angry at the world.

Paul continues.

"I should've been locked up. For a long time, I kind of was—in my mind, if not in a jail cell. After the accident, I spiraled even further out of control. It was like I was punishing myself for what I did to Danny.

"I kept getting into harder and harder drugs until, eventually, heroin became my Higher Power.

"Of course, this way of living led to really quality relationships and I attracted a lot of high-caliber women into my life."

He rolls his eyes at his own particular brand of insanity.

"By twenty-nine, I'd found myself a real winner of a girlfriend who was—wait for it—a stripper *and* a prostitute."

A few people laugh. In AA, tragedy often masquerades as comedy.

"I didn't care that Candi (That was her name—Candi with an *i* of course) was selling herself. As long as she was willing to pay for our H, I was happy. We were together for about a year. Then, one night, around Halloween, Candi told me she was pregnant. It never even occurred to me to ask if I was the father. I was so excited I tossed all our needles, except one, and told her we were gonna get sober. And I made her promise to stop selling herself.

"That night, when Candi left for work, I went down the street and bought a newspaper, so I could look through the classifieds for a job. Well, I *told* myself that's why I left the house. I really went to buy a last six-pack and final bag of H. I figured I'd get high one more time before giving it up for good.

"When I came to, I was on the couch and Candi was dead on the floor in front of me. I still don't know if she used my leftover drugs or if she had a stash of her own. I found out, after her autopsy, that Candi's baby had been dead before her overdose, and that it wasn't mine. Not that it mattered. Having my pregnant girlfriend OD while I was too high to help her was a turning point for me. I finally got desperate enough to change. That was five years ago. I found NA and quit heroin like *that*." Paul snaps his fingers.

"But, even though I haven't picked up H in five years, I still thought I could smoke pot and drink. Stupid. Every time I'd smoke a joint, I'd remember Candi and Danny and descend into a deep, paranoid depression. After a few months of that, I gave up pot too, but I couldn't give up drinking. I'd get a week or two sober from alcohol, then I'd think *I just want one beer* or *a piña colada doesn't count* or *my problem was heroin... drinking is fine*, and I'd be out again, on another bender, drinking until I blacked out.

"I remember coming to these meetings and saying I couldn't stop."

Paul looks around the room. A few of the AA old timers wipe their eyes. They remember him too—the prodigal son, returned at last.

"Back then, I was an atheist. I *knew* there wasn't a God and thought of AA and NA as support groups for people too cheap to pay full price for therapy."

A guy in the back lets out a guffaw, nudges his neighbor, and stage-whispers, "Kid's onto us, Harry. We're a couple a cheap bastards."

Paul continues as if no one's spoken. "I knew these meetings helped, but I didn't understand the spiritual component of the program. Then, one day, I got drunk and went over to my parents' house, found my dad's handgun, and loaded it. But, right before I pulled the trigger, something inside of me, some little whisper, said, 'pray.' So, I did. I said out loud, 'I'm pretty sure there isn't a God, but, in case I'm wrong, please let me go to heaven. Life has been hell enough.' I was praying for relief *after* death. Instead, God gave me something better. I pulled the trigger, and nothing happened. I pulled again and again and... nothing. The bullet had gotten stuck in the chamber.

"For me, that moment, when I said that prayer and pulled that trigger, and something saved me from myself... That was the moment I made the decision to surrender. I still can't say I believed in a God, but I had this sense that there was something bigger than me that had my back. So, I went to a ninety-day rehab facility in New Canaan, Connecticut and got sober.

"I'm not gonna lie. In the beginning, I felt like I'd been tied to the rear bumper of a car and was getting dragged headfirst behind it. Not just physically. Emotionally. Letting go of alcohol was harder than giving up pot or heroin because it meant I couldn't use *anything* to take away my pain—except God. And I still didn't completely believe in God.

"At first, I treated my Higher Power like an imaginary friend. I didn't pray to Him. I prayed because it felt cathartic to say things out loud, and because I was lucky enough to find an awesome sponsor who's been sober for longer than I've been alive. He made me recite the Third Step Prayer every morning and every night—which I did until I found my own conception of a Higher Power and felt comfortable talking to Him in my own words.

"Now, I typically say something like 'HP, you are everything and I am nothing, so please let me do my best to be who you want me to be today.'

"Yup. I call my Higher Power 'HP.' We've got it like that."

Paul intertwines his ring and index finger and everyone laughs.

"Seriously, though, the third step is hard. I mean, what addict likes to surrender?"

I find myself nodding along with everybody else.

"For me, turning my will and my life over meant living in Connecticut for a couple years, because Philly had too many negative associations. It meant no dating and no sex for my first year and a half because, without alcohol, I was too scared of rejection to even talk to a girl.

"It meant learning to be a different person.

"I have to be honest. My surrender is far from perfect, and to say I'm at peace a hundred percent of the time would be bullshit. What happened to Danny still haunts me. Sure, I've made amends to him and his family, but there will never be anything I can do to undo the harm I caused. And, in terms of a Higher Power, I still don't know exactly who or what I believe in. But I do know that I pray and meditate and sponsor other guys and come to meetings and surrender to something larger than myself, and I know that it's that something that's keeping me sober because, on my own, I couldn't go a single day without drinking or using or finding some way to be self-destructive.

"Anyway, thanks for letting me share."

The room erupts into applause.

Hands go up. Frank checks his watch. Everyone who shares after Paul thanks him for his experience, strength and hope, then goes on to say how they relate and to pass along their own third step wisdom.

I don't share. Even though I'm on the third step, I have nothing to contribute.

Plus, as much as I appreciated what he had to say, I don't want to remind Paul I'm here. Luckily, after the meeting, a wave of people rush toward the front of the room to thank him and welcome him back to this city of love because I can feel Paul's eyes on me and am pretty sure, without the buffer, he'd try to talk to me again.

I turn to April and fake a yawn. "This was great. But I'm beat."

She frowns. "A group of us are going out to dinner. You should come."

I glance around. I *am* hungry, yet I'm not about to risk lingering. Not when a certain Birkenstocks-in-winter-wearing smoker might approach.

"The usual?"

"Always."

"I'll meet you there." I sprint toward the door, keeping my head down to avoid having to stop and chat.

"Hello." Salvatore, the host at Pablo's Pizza, and the owner's nephew, smiles at me when I walk through the door.

"Hi."

I'm the first to arrive, so I grab the largest table they've got and promise that the rest of my party will be here any second. Salvatore's used to us—doctors and druggies, construction workers and conmen, housewives and hoboes. It doesn't matter that, outside of AA, we have nothing in common. We talk at full volume, and eat our body weights in cheesy, doughy deliciousness, and tip well because tradition seven teaches us to be self-supporting.

I start to tell the host what I want to drink, but he cuts me off.

"Orange Soda Girl!" he says—like it's my name, as opposed to my preferred beverage. "I gotcha covered."

"Thanks," I tell Salvatore's back, since he's already heading toward the beverage case in the corner.

"Hi."

I turn, startled, to see a smiling Paul standing behind me.

"What are you doing here?"

"A couple of the guys invited me."

Please don't confront me about my coffee-shop standoffishness. And don't sit next to me. I shouldn't have come.

He studies me. "Is that okay?"

Before I can answer, other AAers start trickling in and Salvatore returns with my soda.

"Thanks." I snatch the can and head toward April and as far away from Mr. One Vice Remaining as possible.

"Tell me more about Annabelle and the sex-talk," I order, then only half-listen to my sponsor's answer.

The good thing about AA people is that they expect a certain amount of tempestuousness from the newly sober, so no one gives me a hard time for glowering wordlessly at the Formica tabletop or bogarting the breadsticks. They don't try to get me to talk or ask how I'm doing. Even Paul leaves me alone. Good. I'd rather walk naked down Broad Street in the middle of the Mummers Parade than have a conversation with such a sanctimonious asshole. Now, if he would just stop staring...

"Why are you so jumpy?" April asks.

I look down. My leg is vibrating.

Be still, I order, but my quivering limb ignores my mental mandate. "I should go."

Evidently, my whisper isn't quiet enough because one of the women at our table—Dottie or Dorrie or Donna (some D name)—shouts so loudly I'm pretty sure everyone in the restaurant hears her. "Oh, but Jess, you can't leave yet! Stay! Eat something! A couple breadsticks isn't nearly enough for a meal!"

Damn. Now, I'm even more conspicuous.

I glare at her over my menu.

"Good," April says as I slouch down in my chair. "Fellowship is important—especially in early sobriety."

Even though everyone is chattering over each other, passing plates of food, and telling overlapping "When I was drinking, I used to..." stories, the only voice I hear is the one in my head, warning me to stay away from Paul.

I can't risk falling for him.

Step Four:

Made a searching and fearless moral inventory of ourselves. (Reclining Hero Pose)

31

I've never kept a diary. I've always been too afraid someone might find it, read it, and have me committed. Now, not only do I have to write down everything I've ever done wrong, after I'm done, I have to share it.

April says that, until I own my past, I can't ever break free of it.

According to her suggestion, I'm doing my inventory the *Big Book* way. When she showed me the chart, I told her it seemed like a lot of unnecessary work, but my sponsor reminded me that doing things my way never worked, whereas following her advice has netted me almost six months of consecutive sobriety, so I shut up.

I take a sip of tea. Cinnamon and hazelnut and vanilla bathe my taste buds. Outside, the vestiges of snow remain scattered on the sidewalk. I walk across the room and gaze down at the Lincoln Drive traffic. Not exactly a penthouse view, but a place I can be proud of—especially now that I'm caught up on rent and the landlord has stopped slipping eviction notices under my door. I open and close the refrigerator door. Stare inside for a while. Eat some grapes. Wash, dry, and put away the dishes.

Alright. Enough procrastinating. Time to fill in my chart.

When I finish, seven hours and six snacks later, I tally up the total number of names. 172 people. I've hurt 172 people. It's heartbreaking—and humiliating—to see, in black and white, in my own, unsteady, handwriting, what a selfish, inconsiderate slut I really am.

Hard too given how much I used using to obliterate guilt and shame.

How did I get to be this person?

I examine the chart and try to trace life back to a moment in time when I valued other people more than my own agenda. Instead, I fixate on everyone I've hurt. Not just people I knew either. Strangers who didn't do anything to deserve the ignominy that was me.

Who did I harm?	How did I harm them? What did I do?	Affects my:
Mom	Had sex with her husband, repeatedly Lied to her Stole money from her Ruined family holidays Got drunk and high in her home, disrespected her rules Distanced myself from her	Self-esteem Personal relationships Emotional security Material security
Dwight	Seduced him Had sex with numerous other people and rubbed it in his face Was jealous of him and my mom Was afraid to say no to him, said yes then resented him or was passive-aggressive	Self-esteem Personal relationships Emotional security Sex-relationships Pride Fear Hidden sex relations
Chloe	Wasn't there for her Was a bad sister Missed her birthday, ruined holidays, was unreliable at events Got high and drunk in front of her and exposed her to drugs and sex, repeatedly Stole money from her	Pride Personal relationships Emotional security Material security
Rhonda	Ignored her pain Didn't ask why she was crying Was insensitive to her when she's always been so kind and loving toward me	Self-esteem Personal relationships Emotional security Fear

The window shattered. It wasn't my fault. True, I was the one who thrust my fist through the glass, but I had no choice. He (or was it *she*?) was yelling at me, and I didn't want to get caught.

I was nineteen or twenty—still young enough to pretend there was no such thing as consequences—and my accomplice was roughly the same. We met doing E at a house party in the Lafayette Hill suburbs. I'd shown up with a guy named Harrison who I'd hooked up with at a club the week before.

I'd thought Harrison was cool. He struck me as the kind of person who'd be down for anything. But, when the stranger pulled out a tiny, multicolored pill box that looked as psychedelic as the trips contained within and asked if we wanted to get out of there for a *real* party, Harrison said he wasn't about to leave his friends to get high on questionably-obtained tablets with "some random."

The stranger wasn't random. He or she was a humanitarian. Not everyone is willing to share their stash. But Harrison refused to listen to reason, so I told him he could keep his lame-ass party and the stranger and I headed off on our own. A party of two.

It was snowing. Flakes so large I could see their lacey patterns as I caught them on my tongue. My companion and I danced amidst winter's falling fingerprints and sang off-key to one another, and made snow angels in the backyard of some unknown person's Victorian. The girl (or boy) who'd so generously shared his (or her) pills taught me to do cartwheels on the icy earth while bracing myself so as to avoid a fall. Then, things turned less whimsical.

"Let's break a window," my indeterminately-gendered companion suggested. "Let's steal something."

"That's..." I searched for the right word. "... brilliant!"

We found a house awash in blackness.

"No one's home."

My heart thumped and my palms were sweaty. I'd never stolen from a stranger before. Only from family and friends. As I turned to face my soon-to-be accomplice, he/she started yelling. Not angry yelling. Encouraging. Like a coach, standing on the sidelines, cheering on their star player.

"C'mon, Jess!" he/she shouted. "C'mon! You can do it!"

I thrust my hand into the glass. Blood-stained snow. A pain I was too numb to feel. Standing there, at the threshold of criminality, I couldn't bring myself to enter.

"What're you waiting for, Jess? It's now or never!"

I remained paralyzed, so my new friend crawled through the window while I sat outside on the cold, white ground, trying not to be paranoid. It felt like forever before the front door swung open and my E-companion emerged with a fistful of cash and plastic Acme grocery bag overflowing with beautiful, expensive things. I wore some of those things for a while—necklaces made of precious stones, a gold charm bracelet, dangly earrings, and a promise ring—until I traded them for drugs, or pawned them for cash, which I used to buy drugs. I don't know how I ended up with so much of the loot, especially after being such a lame coconspirator, but I guess he/she didn't judge me on what I didn't do, but on what I did.

"Go, go, go!"

We sprinted back to the thief's Cadillac and drove out of that neighborhood further into the suburban sprawl, where he or she parked in a tiny cul-de-sac, turned off the lights and the wipers, but kept the engine running, the heater on full-blast. Actually, it wasn't his/her Cadillac.

"We should be safe here."

A smile. A hand on my cheek. I'd chickened out once already. There was no backing down again. We climbed into the backseat of a car that didn't belong to either of us (I think it was a loaner from the E-dispensing dude or dudette's grandparents. Or maybe it was stolen. Either way, I remember sitting on someone's AARP card) and fucked in the shadow of our stash.

I didn't ask if the car had been hijacked, or commandeered, or borrowed. And I didn't suggest returning what he or she had taken from a house and a family that, despite all their affluence, would still feel the sting of their loss. Instead, I shut my mouth and opened my legs and enjoyed the high of the forbidden.

Outside, snow is coming down. Not hard, but steady. Flakes—each one with its own unique identity.

The strangest part about my memory of the night I robbed a house and had car-sex with a stranger is that, even though we fucked, I can't remember if my accomplice was a man or a woman.

When did I do that? A downward glance at my notebook reveals that, without realizing it, I've been doodling in the margins of my page. Now, amidst my carefully organized inventory is a makeshift trellis of scribbled roses and flowering heart-shaped buds.

C'mon, Jess. Focus. This is important.

I turn my attention back to my fourth step. Laid out as a series of columns and rows, my actions seem so impersonal. Like random, meaningless, statistical data, or the results of someone else's research survey. But the stories go much deeper than a list of names jotted down in my Barnes & Noble notebook. They're not ink on a page. They're slow-slicing lingchi.

I look at my chart again. It hammers the glass of my delusions, shattering the lie that I was ever a victim.

"You're beautiful."

"Shhh. They'll hear us."

"Who will? Your anal-retentive mom?"

"She's not that bad!"

"Your prissy little sister?"

"Hey!" I protest. "She's my family!" But I'm laughing as I say it.

"Your stepdad, the –"

Before Bruce can complete the sentence, I pull him close and press my lips to his. He tastes like salt and honey—exactly halfway between a boy and a man, at once titillating and inadequate. When he hoists my slender body over one shoulder and twirls me around before tossing me onto my bed, I think, *That's something Dwight could never do with his bad back*. Not that there's not a lot Dwight can do—does do. My sheets are still stained from the previous night's escapade. But Bruce doesn't notice, and I don't care.

Bruce isn't my boyfriend. We just get high together and fool around. Right now, he's half-stoned on weed, half on me. I'm stoned too, but only on the pot.

I strip down in the fully-lit bedroom. I'm not one of those girls who will only do it in the dark. I like to be seen.

Even though the sound of footsteps in the hallway is unmistakable, I don't register their significance, and, when the door swings open, I've got a mouthful of cock.

"Are you fucking kidding me?" Dwight screams.

I didn't lock the door. Was it carelessness or did some secret part of me want to get caught?

I stare at my lover as I wipe the residue of spunk from the tiny crevice between my lip and cheek—the place where, now that I am thirty-two, I've begun to acquire laugh lines. No one is laughing about this.

I turn back to Bruce. For a moment, his pecker, accusatory in its erectness, points at my stepdad.

Way to stand up for yourself, I think.

But his penis is no match for Dwight's anger.

"How dare you!" My stepdad yells.

The cock wilts, impotent in the face of all that rage.

Bruce scoops up his clothes and starts getting dressed. More footsteps. I sit, naked, on the floor, as two additional bodies fill the doorway.

"My God, Jessica." Mom begins to pray. "Hail Mary, full of grace..."

I glower at her, refusing to be shamed.

Bruce, clothed now, but still shoeless, doesn't dare walk past Dwight and Mom and Chloe, so he leaves the same way he came—through my bedroom window. He'll shimmy down my mother's beautiful rose trellis with expert precision. My mother. My poor, tearful, prayerful mother who can't understand why she—a good and decent woman—has a daughter who's as bad as me.

Dwight's face is on fire. So what? He has no right to tell me what—or who—I can and can't do. Not when he spends every night in bed with someone else.

Then, Chloe begins to cry, and, suddenly, I'm painfully aware of my nakedness. I mumble an apology—not for what I've done, but for being dumb enough to get caught—then scramble into my pajamas, crawl beneath the covers, and wait for sleep to save me.

I know Dwight well enough to know he wants to stay and scream, yet Mom and Chloe need his comfort more than I need his criticism, so he leads them down the hall. He'll punish me later. "We're not done with this, young lady!"

The next morning, Sunday, at breakfast, Mom says, "After what she did, I think Jessica should be at church today."

Dwight and I had long since stopped going altogether.

"Why?" he demands. "So she can say a couple Hail Marys and be forgiven for her sins? No. Jesse's gonna stay home and scrub this house from top to bottom and learn that the only way to stop being dirty is to be clean."

Mom appraises me but responds to him. "Alright, darling. You know best."

Chloe refuses to acknowledge me, even when I try to pass her a perfectly golden piece of buttered toast.

"Here." I hold it out.

She finds her own piece—less spectacular, but untainted by my fingers.

I shouldn't be hurt. Or surprised. The line of demarcation—Chloe and Mom on one side, Dwight and me on the other—was drawn a long time ago.

Twenty minutes after Mom and Chloe leave, a yellow van pulls up out front, *Purity Philly* emblazoned on the side. Dwight pre-arranged the service late last night, calling a 1-800 number and paying a premium for a holy-day house scrubbing. But money was the one thing my family never had to be concerned about.

"You've got two and a half hours," he tells the cleaners. "Be out by noon."

Then, he and I head downtown to the Center City Marriott where he's rented adjoining rooms to keep up the pretense of propriety.

"Don't ever let me catch you with anyone else," he tells me after I've submitted to my spanking.

I start to protest that he has no right to be jealous—not when he's *married* to my mom—but he's on me, in me, and if feels too right to risk losing. So, I let my indignation go the way of my innocence.

The weekend after Dwight punished me while Mom and Chloe were at church, I went to a classmate's party and had a threesome with two of Bruce's football buddies.

Bruce wasn't there. He'd gone away for the weekend with his family.

Things with my family were still strained. Mom and Chloe were avoiding me and, although he assured me he wasn't mad anymore, Dwight was being distant. He said it was to keep up appearances, but I could tell he was withholding affection. The few times we managed to do it that week, he refused to look at me.

Bruce's teammates, with their weed and their testosterone, filled a void I simply couldn't tolerate.

When Monday rolled around, Bruce and I were sitting in the cafeteria, splitting a medium fries and turkey BLT, when I casually mentioned the encounter. "You didn't miss much at the party. It was lame. After I fucked Mark and Bobby –"

"What?"

"You didn't miss much."

"You *fucked* another guy? Two other guys?"

"Is that a problem?" My hand hovered over the fries.

Bruce stared at me through wounded eyes. "You know, Jessica, I really loved you."

I withdrew my hand. I didn't want to take one more thing from him. Not after I'd taken too much already. Too late, I realized that I loved Bruce too. But, instead of asking for forgiveness, I pretended to be cavalier. "What's the big deal? It's just sex. It doesn't mean anything." I forced myself to take a fry, slather it in bright red sauce, and chew. "Anyway, it's not like you and I are a couple."

Bruce didn't reply. He simply stood and walked away.

As soon as he was gone, I threw the fries out.

My stomach churned and I knew I couldn't stay at school. I couldn't risk running into Bruce, or Mark, or Bobby.

When I showed up back at home, hours before the designated dismissal time, Mom immediately traded her condemnation for concern. "You okay, Jessica?"

"I ate something that didn't agree with me."

She didn't even scold me for leaving school without permission. She just told me to go lie down. Minutes later, Mom was at my bedside with a hot water bottle and cup of freshly-brewed chamomile.

"Thank you."

I took the cup of her undeserved love, drank it in, and felt better—temporarily.

Back in my apartment, snow dancing in the distance, the smell of cinnamon, hazelnut, and vanilla permeating my warm apartment air, I take a sip and find that my tea has gone cold—a problem I can solve with sixty seconds in the microwave.

A few years after high school, Bruce met a girl in college. They got married and she popped out a couple kids and settled into a Main Line existence that could've been mine if Bruce hadn't walked away because he knew that loving me could only hurt.

Mom sees them now at church on Sundays. Or, at least, she used to. It's been eleven months since the two of us last spoke.

32

"I think you should call your mom back."

"I think you should mind your business."

April and I are sitting on my couch—a mere sixteen miles from the house I grew up in, the house where Mom still lives with the man I want to hate.

"Jess –"

"Seriously, April. I'm not in the mood for a lecture."

My mother called three days ago and left me a cryptic message.

Call me, Jessica—as soon as you can. I need to tell you something about a change in circumstances.

I haven't heard from her in almost a year. I thought about calling her after what happened on the roof (Well, what happened after I fell off the roof), but decided against it. I've broken her heart enough already.

April sighs. "Why'd you tell me if you didn't want my advice? And, p.s., as your sponsor, your life *is* my business."

She's right. She's always right.

"Fine. Wanna know about my life?"

I launch into a mini-monologue about Oliver, Garrett and Trey and how I have an unremitting urge to be someone's someone. I even open up about meeting Paul at Espresso before hearing him speak at the third-step meeting and hating him for being so unhateable. I tell my sponsor that it feels as if I'll never break free of the giant chasm of aloneness in my solar plexus and my fear that I'm doomed to be a slut until the day I die because it's the only way—other than drugs and alcohol—that I can make the feeling of inadequacy go away.

"I think all my drinking and drug use and fucking and lying and stealing and whatnot was about trying to avoid this void," I admit. "I *know* I should be grateful that I have six months sober, but, most of the time, I'm still pretty miserable. And I hate being alone."

When I finish spilling all the secrets I am willing to divulge, April doesn't flinch, or inch away, or scold. She doesn't even blink. "Don't change the subject. Why won't you return your mother's call?"

"Wow. You really cut through the bullshit."

"It's not my first rodeo. Besides, I already knew about the guys."

"You did?"

She smiles. "If you don't want me to find out, you probably shouldn't hook up with men you meet in AA."

Now, it's my turn to smile.

"Your mom…?"

Fuck. She really is relentless.

"I can't imagine what she could possibly need to tell me."

"One more reason to call her."

I toy at the edges of my t-shirt.

"Are you angry at her?"

"Of course not. Why would I be angry at her?"

April shrugs. "Emotions aren't always rational."

"Tell me about it."

I love my mother. I just don't want to see her, talk to her, or listen to anything she has to say. I've spent the last decade and a half constructing a brick wall between us, and the prospect of dismantling it is daunting.

My sponsor wriggles her toes in her sock-clad feet. "Whatever we avoid comes back to bite us in the ass. It might even lead to picking up a drink."

April doesn't know about Dwight. No one knows about Dwight.

If I continue to keep it secret, I'm tying her hands even as I ask her to help me.

I stand. Walk across the room. Walk back. Sit. Stand again. Then return to my initial spot. Finally, when I know I'll never feel ready for the truth and now's as good a time as any, I say, "I was with my stepdad."

April doesn't understand. How could she? Even I don't fully understand. "Meaning…?"

"Meaning, when I was fifteen, I seduced my mother's husband."

A pregnant pause.

"Oh, Jess, I'm sorry."

"Why are you sorry? I'm the one who screwed up."

"You didn't deserve that. Was it kissing? Sex? What happened?"

"It was a relationship. We were together for nearly three years, and we were in love."

I've lied to April so many times, but she's always just looked me in the eyes, her face conveying nothing but belief, and thanked me for sharing. This is different. This is skepticism. And something else. Something my sponsor has never once displayed toward me: pity.

"Dwight and I were in love," I insist. "Really."

April glances at her hands. "I believe that you believe that. But fifteen-year-olds aren't capable of adult relationships."

April doesn't get it. I knew she wouldn't. Dwight's the only one who ever understood.

"Look," I tell her, "I'm just trying to explain why I'm a shitty daughter."

"Okay." She nods. "Thanks for telling me."

We sit, side by side, saying nothing for a while. I fiddle with my phone. No texts. No emails. Nothing to distract from the discomfort.

I put it back on the coffee table.

Cheaply-made wood, bought for $69.99 from IKEA. Not like the furniture at April's, or the stuff I chased Chloe around back when we were still young enough for games.

April breaks the silence. "That's why you don't want to talk to her…?"

"Oh, I *want* to talk to her." As soon as the words escape my lips, I realize that they're true.

Of *course* I want to talk to her. She read me bedtime stories, gave me bubble baths, and let me sleep beside her when I was sick, or sad, or scared. She chased the monsters from beneath my bed, and taught me how to butter toast without contaminating the pristine yellow milkfat with any yucky crumbs. And she forgave me every time I hurt her. How could I not want to wrap myself in the embrace of her voice, as familiar as my childhood baby blanket?

"So, what're you waiting for?"

"I can't face what I did to her."

"Let me get this straight… You hurt her?"

I nod.

"And your *solution* to that is to hurt her more by not returning her call. Yeah, I can see that. That makes sense."

"Alright!" I relent. "I'll call."

Silence expands around us, thick and fragile. This time, I'm the one to break it. "Can you be with me when I do?"

April hands me my cell phone.

I dial Mom's number—familiar, even after all this time.

"You don't store your mother's number in your phone?"

I shrug. Back when I was using, I had a fear that I'd be raped or murdered or bludgeoned with a tire iron and the police would scroll through my phone, find *Mom* in my contact list, and call Mrs. Evangeline Carrington (formerly Mrs. Evangeline Leonard) for a next-of-kin notification. Or, worse yet, that I'd call her myself—under the influence—and tell her the truth.

Mom answers immediately. "Jessica! Thank God!"

"Hi Mom. I'm sorry I haven't called you back. I–"

"He's gone."

"Who's gone?"

"Dwight."

"Is he dead?"

April squeezes my shoulder.

"Oh no. Nothing like that. He… left. Three days ago. I went to the grocery store and, when I came back, he asked for a divorce."

"Out of nowhere?"

"Can you believe it?"

I can't. Or maybe I can. Dwight is a reservoir of broken promises.

"Can you call him?" Mom's tone is that of a child begging for a toy. "Reason with him. He loves you as if you were his own."

"Mom, I haven't spoken to Dwight in… ages. We're not close anymore."

"Please, Jessica. He'll listen to you. I don't know who else to ask." She is pleading—pathetic. "I know he loves me. I think he's having some sort of midlife crisis."

"Okay. I'll make the call." I know, even as the promise spills out of me, that there's no way I can call my stepdad sober.

When I hang up, April is still clutching my hand.

I release her grasp. "How's that for a fucked up family dynamic?"

"Jess, I'm so sorry. I had no idea she'd ask you for something like… Listen, you don't have to go through with –"

I wave away her concern. "It's okay. I'm fine. This whole thing just caught me by surprise."

My sponsor's eyes contain the Spanish inquisition. If I'm not careful, they'll bore through me until I feel compelled to confess.

"I think I need a nap," I say. "You know…? To hit my emotional reset button."

"Want me to stay?"

My fake smile stretches across my lips, harder to hold than any yoga pose. "What for? To watch me sleep?"

April studies my face. "Will you call me when you wake up? You can come over. I can take you to a meeting."

"Sure."

"Promise you won't call him without me. You don't even have to call him at all. We should talk about it more—after you get some rest."

I don't want to tell April something that isn't true, so I nod and let my head do my lying for me.

"Some things are difficult. Even in sobriety." My sponsor hugs me—hard. "*Especially* in sobriety," she amends.

"Really, April, don't worry. I can handle this."

From my vantage point at my living room window, I watch my mentor walk outside, get into her BMW, and pull away from the curb. But I don't move right away. Instead, I wait as the seconds on my digital watch to tick upward until they trigger the minutes to change, then begin again at zero and count up until the next minute increase and its subsequent plunge into nothingness. Finally, after five minutes—three hundred seconds—when I'm certain April isn't coming back, I put on my coat, drive to the liquor store, and make a purchase. Then, I stop at the intersection of Fifth Street and Carpenter before heading home.

33

First step: text Dwight. I don't want to do anything I'll regret unless I know he's available to talk.

Hey, I type. Can you talk?

His reply arrives immediately. *Sure.*

I'll call you in five.

I stare down at my phone and the bottle of Patrón.

I should call April. Or pray. Or meditate. Or go to a yoga class. Or do anything other than what I'm about to do. But nothing else will suffice. So I uncork the bottle.

A glass is unnecessary. There is nothing refined about this moment.

I spread my lips and open—wide and receptive. The Patrón is strong. Pungent. Biting. Astringent. It scorches my esophagus. I take several swigs, then gulp water directly from the kitchen faucet, my hands forming a makeshift cup as I shovel liquid into my body, putting out a fire of my own making.

"Hey kiddo." Dwight sounds exactly as I remember.

"Why'd you leave her?" I don't bother with small-talk. My stepdad is the only person who's never expected me to pretend.

He sighs. "So many reasons. We had a thirty-minute conversation about trans fats. She wanted me to check my cholesterol."

"And that's a problem?"

"It's all a problem. Everything she cares about, I don't. It's so... boring."

Has he been drinking too? I can't tell if he's slurring his words or if the Patrón is playing tricks inside my skull.

"It didn't used to be boring. You used to be happy."

"Not with her."

I take another sip.

"It hasn't been the same since you left."

"I left fourteen years ago."

"Exactly. Your mother and I were fourteen years past our expiration date."

"Dwight, Mom loves you. I have no idea why she loves you, but she loves you."

"No idea. Really?"

The question hangs in the air like a white flag of surrender after a brutal, bloody war. Dwight sees only the promise of something new waving in the breeze. I see the bodies, piled unceremoniously, rotting in the noonday sun.

"You were it for me, Jesse. For a while, being with her was like being with an extension of you, which made it better. Then, it made it worse."

I force my voice to remain even and cold, but there's nothing I can do about my heart. "That's so lame."

"If I go back to her, will you come back to me?"

"What? How can you ask me that?"

There is the unmistakable clink of ice in a glass. I close my eyes and envision his long, strong fingers caressing that smooth, transparent vessel.

"I hate myself for what we've done," I tell him.

"I love you," he replies.

"I love you too, Dwight."

I look down at the line of chalk on my kitchen table—like the beginning of a miniature hopscotch game.

"You hurt me." I take another swallow. It goes down more smoothly this time.

"I know."

In the background, I hear someone else—a woman. "Dwight, come to bed." Her voice is aspartame sweet.

"Who's that?"

"Be right there!" my stepdad tells her. He muffles the phone while they exchange a few inaudible words. When he returns his focus to me, he isn't apologetic or ashamed. He's the Dwight I remember. The Dwight of my childhood. "She's a warm body. Someone to pass the time and help me forget."

"I can't forget," I admit. "I've tried."

He misunderstands my meaning. "I can't forget you either."

I refuse to be nostalgic. "Look, are you going back to Mom or not?"

"Evangeline..." His exhalation drags on forever—an enviable feat, even for a yogi like me. And he's not even trying. "Evangeline," he says again. "She's a good woman. Easy and kind and moral and unexciting. Jesse, I don't want a good woman. I want you."

I bend down, straw in hand, and inhale what is not chalk or a game or a way to recapture the innocence of childhood. I feel the old, familiar burn in the back of my nose and the numbness in my nostrils.

"She loves you," I repeat.

"I love you." He pulls the ripcord of connection. Only, there is no parachute. Not this time.

There's nothing left to say, except goodbye. Dwight will go back to the bed and the girl and I will go back to my sad, sober life. Only, I'm not sober anymore.

I hang up, run to the bathroom, lean over the toilet, and throw up.

34

I wake to three text messages, two voicemails from my sponsor, and a text from Carla telling me to call her because she has good news. I let the phone lie, unplugged and running out of battery, on my night table as I drag myself out of bed.

The rank odor of putrefaction, of partially digested foodstuff and liquor, lingers. So, I find some all-purpose Lysol with bleach and scrub away the vomit. In the kitchen, when I withdraw the wet sponge from its stainless steel sink basin and ring out all it's been holding onto, its smell assails my nostrils, but I refuse to get a clean, new one until I've wiped the leftover cocaine off the kitchen table, poured the remaining Patrón down the sink, and let the running water chase my bad decisions down the drain.

In front of the open fridge, I take out a handful of grapes, shoving them into my mouth in an unwashed clump. They are as sweetly delicious as I remember, a far better palate cleanser than the Listerine I swish around my mouth until it burns my tongue and in between teeth.

It's not until I crawl back into bed that I let myself sob.

Six months of sobriety lost, and for what? A single, failed phone call.

I've let Mom down. April down. Myself down. My eyes want to close—to shut out the world and its inescapable realities—but there's one thing I have to do first. I pick up my phone. It still has some life left. Enough for this excruciating task.

"Hi, Jessica."

"Hi, Mom."

I wait.

She waits.

I take a deep breath and shatter her hope. "I'm sorry. He said no."

Shame descends like an avalanche.

I rush to the rescue with empty reassurances. "He loves you, Mom. He says you're a good woman."

"Did he say why?" Her words come out high-pitched and hiccuppy.

"No. You're probably right—about the midlife crisis."

She sniffles. Collects herself. My mother does everything gracefully—including falling apart. I don't know what else to say, so I keep my mouth shut and listen while the person I've betrayed most often and most egregiously tells me about the full scope of her heartbreak.

"This isn't like with your dad. Letting go of someone when there's no possibility of them ever coming back is less painful than letting go when your heart still has hope."

Remorse swims to the surface of my emotional muck and bobs on its top, like a corpse that's broken free of its concrete moorings and surfaced in the Passaic, also known as "New Jersey's river of death."

"I can't believe I lost him," she says, unaware that I took Dwight from her long before he ever left.

I remember Rhonda telling us in class once that lotus flowers grow out of muck. "There is beauty to be found in even the ugliest of places."

There's no flowering here. Never was.

"I love you, Mom."

It's too late. She's already hung up. My only answer is a dial tone.

I spend the rest of the day shivering in bed, wishing for sleep that doesn't come, wanting to undo everything that happened after April walked out the door.

35

Carla found Rhonda. That was her big surprise. My friend texted me again, this morning, and demanded I meet her in Flourtown, where our favorite teacher has found a home at a new studio.

C'mon, Jess. I know you don't have anything (or anyone) better to do.

I crawl into class, hung-over, bleary-eyed, and feeling like death. Once again, I've fallen down the rabbit hole of relapse. It's been two days since my slip. Two days of tearful self-recrimination. A forty-eight-hour pity-party, thrown by me, for me.

Branches is refreshingly unpretentious, painted pale, sun-ray yellow with a white Tree of Life stencil etched onto its solid, stable surface. It's been three weeks since I last took a class with Rhonda and my body is craving whatever modes of redemption she can offer.

"Double Pigeon Pose will open your hips," she says. "And, since your hips are a doorway into shame, don't be surprised if feelings come up."

Carla went to a lot of trouble to track our beloved teacher down, and, now, here she is, looking ordinary as ever, spouting precious pearls of wisdom, which I cling to like my mother to her well-used rosary beads.

"If we sit in our shame long enough, we move through it. It's only by trying to avoid it, distract from it, or obliterate it that we deepen our self-hatred."

I let out an involuntary laugh.

Rhonda glances at me.

Quickly, laughter turns to sadness and a tide of tears erodes the gritty surface of my sand. This isn't funny. It's tragic. My teacher continues talking. She knows tears are healing.

"Be attentive to what your body is trying to tell you. Listen to it. Feel your physical sensations, and your emotions. Be grateful for each new revelation."

Rhonda is not a fast and loose dispenser of tissues. Joy, she tells us, is on the other side of suffering. The only way to get to it is by passing through the pain.

It is in Shavasana that Rhonda lays her hands on me. She hasn't adjusted me at all this practice, and I've mistaken her lack of attention for a lack of affection. But, as my teacher rubs my shoulders, massages my temples, and gently caresses my hair, I know I've been projecting my own self-judgments onto her. And I know what I have to do.

* * *

After class, Carla wants to linger, but it's 7:45 and, if I hurry, I can make the Monday Night Beginners meeting.

"Can't," I tell her. "Thanks though."

"For what?"

"Your friendship. And for finding Rhonda. I didn't know how much I needed this."

"You okay? You seemed off tonight and –"

I enfold her in my arms, letting my hug convey what I lack the words to articulate.

I'm not okay. But I will be, provided I can learn from my mistake.

"I need a meeting."

"Alright. If you wanna talk afterward, I'll be up late. Tim is staying at his boyfriend's place tonight."

"I'll call you."

As I drive away, I know that I will call Carla later tonight and share the secret shame of having lost my grip on sobriety and she'll listen and understand and accept me unconditionally, not because she has to, but because she's decided that I am worthy of her love.

* * *

April is at the meeting, as I know she will be, even though I haven't called or texted since I watched her walk out my building door. She takes her purse off the chair beside her. "I'm glad you came."

"I screwed up."

"You're human. You came back. That's all that matters."

I open my mouth to say something—anything—that will make her give up on me, but, for the first time, I don't want to prove my sponsor wrong.

8:00. The meeting starts. I put my hand up—desperate to share before I lose my nerve.

"My name is Jessica and I'm an alcoholic. I relapsed two nights ago, after six months of sobriety. I picked up because, when I was younger, I was sexually abused by my stepdad and I've been refusing to deal with it. My mom asked me to call him, and I did, and I didn't think I could get through it without taking the edge off. But I don't wanna blame my slip on other people. I've done enough of that already. My stepdad isn't the reason I relapsed. I picked up because I can't stop punishing myself for the past. Thanks for letting me share."

I've admitted the unspeakable in a room full of people. Yet, rather than feeling like an outcast, I feel more included than ever. Like the walls that have surrounded me my entire adult life are finally coming down. Every face in the room turns to look at me—to *really* look at me. Their eyes are a labyrinth of love. Maybe, if I can start to see myself as they see me, I'll be able to navigate my way out of this maze.

36

"But I lied to you," I point out—again.

Even on the phone, I can hear the shrug in April's tone. "You're an addict. Addicts lie."

At last night's meeting, my sponsor made it clear she forgave me for my relapse, but in the shamed and sober light of day, I find myself seeking reassurance. That's the thing about my addict brain. It forgets things I know to be true.

"But you were trying to help me." I lie back at my unmade bed and stare at the ceiling.

"No. I was trying to help—I *am* trying to help—myself."

"Huh?"

"Working with you keeps me from picking up."

She's told me this before, but, to me, sponsorship seems like one more thankless chore of recovery.

"Stop wallowing in your shit," April orders. "Are you sober today?"

"Yes..."

"Do you understand that you're powerless?"

"Absolutely."

"Well, then, the only thing to do is learn from what happened and keep moving forward."

I hesitate before asking the question that's been on my mind since I dispensed with all my hard-won sobriety. "Does this mean I have to start over?"

"Well... That depends. Do you think your relapse happened because you're unwilling to surrender, or because you're ashamed of your past?"

"My past—definitely."

"Then, it's time to do your fifth step."

"I'm not ready."

"You're not ready to let go of your regrets so you can finally stop hating yourself and screwing up your life?"

Put that way, I have no choice but to agree to spill my sins to another sober soul.

"We'll do it Saturday," she decides. "Howie can watch the girls. In the meantime, pick a place."

"What kind of place?"

"Somewhere that feels safe and nurturing. Somewhere where you can feel the presence of your Higher Power."

It takes me three days to decide on a location.

I think about going to a church, but there's not enough stained glass in the world to filter out the dark associations of slutty Sundays and lies told in the shadow of a lectern. And, because I'm not Jewish, or Muslim, synagogues and mosques hold no significance for me. My apartment is a no-go. I've used here. I've had indiscriminate sex here. I could ask to go to April's, but the fifth step demands privacy and I'm not about to ask Howie and the girls to clear out just so their wife and mother and I can have their house to ourselves. Besides, it's too much like the house I grew up in.

Finally, on Friday, the day before April and I intend to do my fifth step, I call her and tell her that, even though it'll be forty-three degrees, I feel most spiritual outside—not so much in nature as surrounded by the stream of life—so I've settled on Love Park.

Step Five:

Admitted to God, to ourselves, and to another human being the exact nature of our wrongs. (Bridge Pose)

37

On Saturday morning, my ringing cell phone wakes me up.

"We still on?" April wants to know.

"It's seven o'clock. We said ten."

"Ten it is. Dress in layers because we're gonna sit there until you're done." She hangs up.

Three hours later, we meet in front of the four familiar letters. April has brought two folding chairs, a blanket, two bottles of water (one for each of us), and a thermos full of hot chocolate to share. I've brought myself and my step-journal, clutched tightly to my chest. We find a relatively quiet place where my sponsor immediately begins constructing an outdoor confessional while I try to think of plausible last-minute excuses for not doing this today.

I'm not ready.

I just relapsed.

There are too many people around.

There aren't. In February, very few Philadelphians are in the mood to sit and chat outdoors. Anyone who happens past is walking—briskly—by and won't slow down long enough to overhear my admissions.

Saturday's not a holy enough day. We should do it on a Sunday. No. Not tomorrow, Sunday. Two days in a row of watching his own kids is too much of an imposition on Howie. We should wait at least a week before asking your husband to babysit again.

It's chilly out. Let's wait until Spring.

"You ready?"

"Not really."

"Good. Let's start by saying the Third Step Prayer together."

God, I offer myself to Thee — to build with me and to do with me as Thou wilt. Relieve me of the bondage of self, that I may better do Thy will. Take away my difficulties, that victory over them may bear witness to those I would help of Thy Power, Thy Love, and Thy Way of life. May I do Thy will always!

We sit.

I read.

One by one, I recount each of the harms I've perpetuated—both in and out of addiction. I don't just tell April what I've done. I tell her who I am.

"I'm a user. I've had sex with men for money and drugs. I chose boyfriends based on their access to weed. I treated people like objects."

I tell about the night my mother had a miscarriage and how surprised I was when she came, knocking, on my door. By then, we'd already begun to feel oceans apart, but, when she was drowning in her sadness, she came to me—the shark—to save her. I held her while she bled and told her I loved her and that, sometimes, life could be cruel, even to its angels. Then, I asked if she wanted something to take away the pain.

When she said yes, I gave her two Xanax. In those days, I always had a stash. Mom took the pills, her eyes wet with tears. "Thank you."

She didn't ask where the drugs had come from, and I didn't offer any explanations. I was relieved to be able to take away her hurt. Later that night, while she was passed out, Dwight came to me with tears in his eyes. I took away his pain too.

"When I was seventeen, I got an abortion," I tell April. "I don't know who the father was, but I know who it could've been."

She squeezes my knee.

On the Boulevard, a horn honks. Traffic advances—a procession of cars on their way from one destination to another.

"I couldn't have raised a baby. I was getting high every day and could barely take care of myself."

I haven't thought about my trip to Planned Parenthood in years. I try never to think about it. It's not that I have qualms about a woman's right to choose. It's just that I didn't feel like I made a choice. My options were restricted by addiction. Or, maybe, I did make a choice. The choice was to keep using, no matter what the cost. Sometimes, I'll see a mother holding her baby, remember the embryo that was suctioned out of me, and wonder if I lost my only chance to have a family of my own.

April reaches out a gloved hand and wedges it between the pages of my journal—like a bookmark—forcing me to look up and make eye-contact. "I had one too," she admits. "Back when I was using. Sometimes, things that feel irrevocable aren't."

"And, other times, they are."

I tell April about the night when, in a drunken haze, I accidentally ran over the neighbor's cat. I didn't mean to. I didn't see it. I felt it.

When I climbed out of the car, the sight of matted red calico fur made me want to hurl. Instead, I climbed back inside, restarted the engine, and continued on toward home. I knew I should tell someone, but I was driving drunk and didn't want to get in trouble.

For days afterward, a dark red stain remained on our quiet stretch of cul-de-sac. It wasn't until the rain washed it away, and the family buried a shoebox in the backyard, that I could bring myself to wave at them across our lawns again. A week after the cat funeral, I sold the grief-stricken neighbor boy our family dog. Then, when my mother called around looking for Santa Cruz and the boy's mother told her that her son had brought the dog home a few days before saying I'd given it to him in exchange for his allowance, I lied.

I looked that poor little pissant straight in his teary eyes and said, "I never sold you our dog."

So what if the kid had lost a cat? I'd lost a *dad*. He'd get over his grief, just as I had gotten over mine.

"That's it," I say after confessing my two suicide attempts.

I've read the last of what I've written. The journal page beyond this one is blank.

"Is there anything you haven't told me?" April asks. "Any details you've knowingly omitted?"

Something about the way her vocal inflection makes it clear she doesn't see me any differently gives me permission to tell the final, brutal truth. I've never told anyone the secret I've harbored since I was five.

"I'm responsible for my dad's death."

Before Daddy died, he'd refused to let me stay up late and eat ice cream with him, and I was so mad I screamed "I *HATE* you! I wish you were dead!"

Then, I stormed upstairs, slammed the door, and told God I wished he'd make me an orphan, like Oliver in the movie with the singing dogs, so I could do what I wanted and not have to answer to anybody.

The next morning, Daddy, intent on replacing a loose shingle, climbed onto our roof, slipped, fell, and severed his spine. For the three days he was in a coma, I refused to visit. I told myself that, if I'd had the power to wish him dead, I also had the power to wish him back to life. All I had to do was focus all of my attention on making him okay again. Then, God would resurrect him. Like Jesus.

"Is that what you've been punishing yourself for all these years? Because you wished your dad would die, and he did."

I nod. "That and not seeing him, at the end, when I had the chance."

April smiles. "Wow. You really are self-centered."

My watery eyes blink their surprise. "What?"

"You know how many kids wish their parents dead every day? Erika once threw a doll at my head and said she wished I wasn't her mommy. Then, an hour later, she climbed into my lap, asked me to read her a story, and said I was, and I quote, 'the best mommy ever.' Being a shithead is part of being a child."

"Is it?" Consciously, I know the answer, but my subconscious requires reassurance.

"Hell, yes! Show me a kid who never rebels, and I'll show you an adult with some serious psychological problems. Kids are supposed to act out. It's healthy."

I smirk. "Oh yeah, I'm a beacon of health."

"And powerful too, don't forget. Powerful enough to kill someone with your thoughts."

Suddenly, we are laughing. Laughing at the enormity of my ego and the insanity of my long-harbored guilt about something that should've been so easily forgiven.

"It's good to get that out. I've been holding onto that for twenty-seven years."

"And seeing your dad shouldn't have been your decision. You were a *child*. Your mom should've insisted you go."

Instead, I stayed home with a babysitter while, each day, Mom strapped Chloe in her car seat, drove four miles away, to Bryn Mawr Hospital, and didn't return again for hours.

"I guess I made a lot of decisions I wasn't old enough to make."

My stomach growls. A look at my watch tells me that April and I have been sitting in Love Park for four hours.

"I can't believe it's after two."

My sponsor reads my mind. "How about some lunch?"

"How about HipCityVeg?" People in my yoga classes have been raving about the vegan and vegetarian hotspot for weeks, and, even though I have no interest in some bullshit can't-eat-anything-with-a-face-because-I'm-enlightened (aka yogic) diet, after having unburdened myself of so much emotional waste, I'm craving clean, healthy food.

"So what do you think?" my sponsor asks as we walk the three blocks to the restaurant. "Was step five as bad as you thought it'd be, or did it make you feel free to unburden yourself?"

"It wasn't as bad as I thought," I concede.

And, even though I can't say I feel free, I do feel lighter.

Part III

Pose

Handstand (Adho Mukha Vrksasana)

Stand up straight with your feet comfortably apart and your arms lifted toward the sky. Your feet, knees, torso and head should all be aligned and completely vertical. Take a big step forward with one leg (typically your dominant leg, although it is good to practice alternating legs). As you step, let your body tip over your lunged leg. Hold your arms straight as your hands approach the ground. Keep tension in your shoulders, and, as you lift your legs, engage your core to bring your torso vertical. Keep your legs tightly together and balance your weight evenly on your hands. (Remember: A Handstand should be entered into in one smooth, fluid motion).

Prayer

Seventh Step Prayer

My Creator, I am now willing that you should have all of me, good and bad. I pray that you now remove from me every single defect of character which stands in the way of my usefulness to you and my fellows. Grant me strength, as I go out from here, to do Your bidding.

Promise

"We may have had certain spiritual beliefs, but now we begin to have a spiritual experience. The feeling that the drink problem has disappeared will often come strongly." (*Alcoholics Anonymous Big Book*, p. 75)

Step Six:

Were entirely ready to have God remove all these defects of character. (Standing Split)

38

I arrive at Branches an hour early on purpose. Rhonda's Sunday afternoon students are long gone, but the lights are on, and the girl at the desk smiles at me over the top of her magazine.

"I live too far away to go home," she explains, "so I'm waiting around for the next class to start."

"Is it okay if I set up my stuff?"

"Totally." She returns her attention to the Kardashians.

As soon as I'm alone in the empty studio room, I unroll my yoga mat, sink to my knees, settle my hips back onto my heels, and cry until my mat is soaked. I haven't ever grieved like this before—from a place of finality and acceptance. Yet, in the safe and sheltered space of Child's Pose, I find the soft solace of my breath and focus on inhaling and exhaling until the words I need to say come to me.

Through a veil of tears, my five-year-old self surfaces and speaks to the man she never said goodbye to when she had the chance. "I'm sorry, Daddy. I didn't want you to die. I shouldn't have yelled at you, and I should've gone to the hospital..."

Words spill out of me like blood from the dying, a torrent of messy, disgusting, life-containing truths. I hadn't realized how many liters of longing were contained within my body.

The chalkboard of men's names—episodes scrawled in front of me, tallying my attempts to obliterate my pain with drugs and sex and alcohol—that my sponsor tells me can only be erased if I'm willing to believe in something greater than myself.

"I made so many mistakes, and I hate myself for what I did—for all the things I've done. I don't know why I keep looking for men to take away the emptiness, but I miss you, Daddy, and I don't understand why you had to die."

At some point during my rambling monologue, I realize that I've found a Higher Power—someone loving and paternal, with a shock of white in his hair, who loves me even when I make mistakes.

I move to the top of my mat, grab the bottom of my right foot with both hands, and stand in Utthita Hasta Padangusthasana.

With my leg outstretched, I don't feel precarious. I feel strong, grounded, and balanced. "If you were here," I say, "I know you'd forgive me. And I'd like it if you could help me forgive myself." Then, I move my mat to the wall and practice my handstands for the next fifteen minutes, until people start to trickle in.

By the time the door opens and the next student enters what feels like my own temporary sanctuary, I am alive with the exhilaration of inversions.

Long before I sprouted breasts, or got my period, or grew hair in places that require shaving, I loved handstands. And cartwheels. And somersaults.

During the 1990 US Gymnastics Championships, I insisted on watching all the vault, uneven bar, balance beam, and floor routines. I even made cutout cardboard score cards and held them up to the TV to see if my rankings matched those of the judges. At night, and in the morning, I practiced on my bed until I made so much noise Mommy and Daddy came in, found my pillows strewn around the room, and ordered me outside.

"This is a bedroom, young lady, not a gymnasium. Walter, what are we going to do with her?"

"I dunno, Evangeline. Enroll her in gymnastics?"

At Daddy's urging, Mommy signed me up.

A few years after I enrolled, she arrived one afternoon an hour into our two-hour practice and announced that I had to leave early because I had a dentist's appointment.

I threw a fit.

"I won't go!" I somersaulted and cartwheeled and tuck-and-rolled away, refusing to stop, or even slow, until Mom snuck up on one side, my teacher on the other, and the two of them wrangled me out to the car.

"Jessica!" My mother was simultaneously exasperated and empathetic. "Sweetheart, I don't understand why you're so afraid. It's just a cleaning."

"I'm not afraid. I just don't want to miss class."

My favorite thing about ground and aerial acrobatics was the rush of not yet having landed. Yet, it wasn't enough to simply experience the high of being suspended. I needed a witness.

After Daddy died, but before Rodney, and long before Dwight, Mom took Chloe and me to the shore house. While she lay on her star-spangled blanket, staring off into space, my sister and I played for hours in the sand.

The blanket had been a joke—purchased from a Fourth of July vendor in the early days of her and Daddy's dating. They'd been strolling, hand-in-hand, down Nantucket's' cobblestone streets, and she said, "Now, that may be the tackiest thing I've ever seen." So, he bought it for her. And, even though they'd had it longer than I'd been alive, and it had started to pill, he insisted on bringing it out for parch picnics and trips to the beach.

"That ugly thing?" Mom would shake her head whenever she saw it. "Walter, isn't it about time we threw that out?"

But, on those sweltering summer afternoons, in the aftermath of his involuntary abandonment, she'd ensconce herself in false patriotism and stare—glassy-eyed—into the distance, as if expecting him to emerge from the water. We were the same then, Mom and I. I too expected Daddy's death to be revealed as an illusion.

"Mommy, Mommy, watch me!" I kicked my legs into the air and somersaulted out of my handstand into a haphazard tuck-and-roll.

She smiled wanly, not really paying attention. I showed off more. She looked a little further off, toward something—or someone—that never came.

"Why aren't you watching? I'm trying to show you!"

"Jesus, Jessica! When are you gonna realize you're not the center of the universe?"

Her words hit me like a slap across the face and I fled from the beach to my shore house bedroom where I crawled inside the closet and barricaded myself behind a wall of stuffed animals.

Mommy didn't knock. She simply swung the door open. "I'm sorry, Jessica. I didn't mean to snap. I'm sad right now and missing your daddy."

"I miss him too."

"I pray every night not to be alone."

I pray every night for Daddy to come back to us.

"Can you understand that it's not only hard for you, but also hard for Mommy?"

I nodded.

"That's my girl."

I crawled out from the softness into her insubstantial arms and let her believe I understood, and, when we got back to the Bryn Mawr house, I told her I wanted to quit gymnastics and she told me she'd put the Cape May house on the market. We wouldn't be going back there anymore.

"It's just not fun without your father," she said.

I didn't argue. She was right. And, even though I was still fully capable of suspending myself upside-down, I stopped doing handstands—because no one was watching, and nobody cared.

39

I walk into the Friday Night Weekenders Meeting and immediately start salivating at the finest piece of eye candy I've ever laid eyes on. Classically gorgeous with a chiseled chin, broad shoulders, dark curly hair, baby blues, and a lethal smile, the guy is an animated fantasy.

So much for my newfound awareness. The familiar compulsion to wrap my arms and legs around a stranger and call out his name (a name I won't remember in the morning) rises up from my Sacral Chakra, as ripe and juicy as an orange. I bite into it and let the sweet, sinful nectar drip down into me. Paul's here too, grinning at me from the front row, but I can't be bothered with a reformed bad boy. Not when the real thing is available.

We don't even bother to conceal our motives. As soon as the meeting ends, I gesture to the hottie. He smirks at me and, in tandem, we head toward the door.

Outside, as the cold night-after-Valentine's-Day air nips at our ears, he's the first to speak. "One car or two?"

"Two's easier. That way, when we're done, we can go our separate ways."

He approves. "Smart thinking."

"My place or yours?"

"Either is cool. I live just over the bridge in Cherry Hill."

"Let's go to mine." I live a mile and a half away and am not looking to be inconvenienced.

"Nice place," he says after we're inside. He's eyeing me though, not my apartment.

I close my door. Lock it behind us. Lead him to my bedroom. Unbutton my pants. Strip off his shirt.

We fuck on autopilot. Sixty miles an hour and clear skies straight ahead.

"Oh yeah. Oh, Baby."

His body is hard and perfectly chiseled. Mine is human. As we engage in the familiar act of friction, I find myself trying to forget.

"Harder. Faster."

He obeys.

I pretend to cum.

It's not that the sex is bad—I've certainly had worse—but there's no sense of connection and, frankly, I'm relieved when we can give up the charade.

On his way out the door, I kiss the stranger goodbye, but I don't offer him my number, and he doesn't ask for it.

"Great to meet you," he says.

"See you around," I reply.

I don't walk him downstairs or stand at my window and watch him drive away. His being gone is a relief. Yet, it initiates an old, all-pervasive ache. Whatever wound I was trying to stitch together with anonymous sex has only gotten more infected—as if I tried to put a Band-Aid on an amputation.

Back in bed, beneath my sex-stained sheets, I pray to the father who used to tuck me in at night. "I don't know why I did that. I want to be different, but I also want to be wanted. Please, Daddy, if you're up there, or out there, teach me how to be a better person."

Then, I close my eyes, crash into sleep, and let my dreams offer a reprieve.

≠ 40 ≠

I'm trying to be better about getting to meetings early so I can interact with people and be at least marginally helpful. Since we met, April has been reminding me of the well-known AA adage "Meeting makers make it."

"Right. And I'm making it to a lot of meetings and staying sober."

"Everyone always gets that wrong."

"What do you mean?"

"It's not 'meeting makers make it' as in people who make it to a lot of meetings make it. It's people who help make meetings happen—by doing service—who stay sober."

So, here I am, twenty minutes early, ready to lend a helping hand.

Unfortunately, I'm not the only one.

Paul looks up from setting up chairs and smiles. "Two nights in a row. Lucky me." His eyes are clear and judgment-free. "Wanna give me a hand with these?"

I hesitate. Why's he being so friendly? Doesn't he know I'm damaged? Who but I have one-night stands with men she meets at meetings?

"Grab one or two more from there." He points at a pile of folding chairs in the corner. "And help form a circle."

We work in silence for a while. It feels good to be useful for a change.

"You know, Jess, I'd like to get a cup of coffee with you sometime."

I raise an eyebrow. "Is that a euphemism?"

"Nope. It's a beverage."

"Look, Paul, you may not know this, but I've already fucked four guys in AA." (Well, three and a half).

"Then it's a good thing I don't want to fuck you."

I give him my *yeah right!* look.

"Alright." He chuckles. "Maybe, one day. But, for now, I just wanna get to know you. Maybe, take you on a date."

"Why would you want to date me? You've been sober for two years and I've been sober for a minute." I'm not looking to repeat what happened with Trey. Or Oliver. Or Garrett. Or the nameless stranger from last night.

Paul seems surprised. "I thought you had six or seven months."

"I had a slip."

“I’m sorry to hear that.” His eyes are devoid of guile. “Well, Jess, that doesn’t change how I feel about you. I liked you the moment I met you.”

I give him my patented raised-eyebrow glare.

He laughs. “Exactly. You were angry and standoffish, and full of something else, something I couldn’t put my finger on...”

“Spite?” I’m only half-joking.

“That too.” His tone turns serious. “Honestly, Jessica, you’re a loveable person. Just because you can’t see it in yourself doesn’t mean I don’t see it in you.”

You’re pretty loveable yourself is what I want to say. I even open my mouth to form the words. Only, they melt on my tongue like lozenges—syrupy sweet and completely ineffectual. I want to tell Paul I want to be the kind of girl a guy like him could fall for, but that, unless I change, I’ll break his heart and, frankly, I like him too much to do that to him.

Instead, I stand, like an idiot, clutching the edge of a flimsy metal chair while Paul leans down and kisses me tenderly on the lips in front of all the incoming anonymous people. “When you’re ready, let me know, because I’m pretty sure I could fall for you.”

41

When I arrive at her front door armed with my yoga mat, a box of microwave popcorn and my bootlegged copy of *Girl Interrupted*, Carla's eyes are bleary and bloodshot. I don't have to ask what's wrong. We're becoming the kind of friends who can fill in each other's blanks. It's about her husband—Tim. For Carla, everything is about Tim, just as my pain has always been about the unavailable men in my life. I'm starting to see that drugs and alcohol weren't so much the *cause* of my problems as my bass-awkward *solution* to them.

"He moved out today!" she wails. "Officially. He's living with his boyfriend."

I hand her a soda. "It's okay to fall apart."

We don't get to the yoga or the movie. Instead, Carla and I spend the night demolishing the popcorn, drinking Diet Coke until we belch great, reverberating, carbonated belches, and talking about the painful process of falling in and out of love.

"Who was your first love?" she asks.

I hesitate. I loved Dwight, yet, somehow, I don't think that qualifies. Our relationship was too messy and paternal. I loved Bruce, but not in that rapturous, all-consuming, committed way that sends butterflies to your stomach and makes you feel dreamy. Certainly not the way he loved me. Over the years, I've convinced myself that a dozen or so men were *the one*. But were they really?

I used to think getting high intensified my ability to feel. Now, I know that intoxication stripped me of the capacity for intimacy.

"I don't think I've ever been in love," I admit.

"I hadn't either, until I met Tim. He's so different from anyone I'd ever dated. I mean, he's sweet and sensitive and beautiful. Most of the Asian men I've gone out with have been cold and walled-off. I think it's a cultural thing. My father has ice in his veins. Tim has the most open heart." She glances at the framed photo on the mantle—she in a gorgeous red dress and Tim in a white suit with a gold cummerbund and bright red pocket square. "On our wedding day, he promised to be with me forever. We both cried. I never thought... I mean, he was my soul... I can't..."

"I understand," I tell her, because I do. Falling for the wrong person isn't something you can rationalize away.

"I know he's gay. I just can't get myself to stop loving him."

"So, let yourself love him. Don't fight the impulse."

Carla takes another sip of her soda.

"Love him *and* let him go," I advise.

"Like in yoga..."

"What do you mean?"

"You know how we feel our feelings without becoming attached to them?"

She's right. That's exactly what we do in yoga.

As my friend wraps me up in her slender-armed embrace, I can't help but think about how the mat is a mirror image of the sixth step. I can't change whatever crazy ideas or destructive impulses arise in life any more than I can change the diversionary thoughts that come during a yoga class. The only difference is, in yoga, I've learned not to try. Every time my mind wanders, I simply bring myself back to focusing on my breath. Maybe, the essence of becoming entirely ready to let go of my character defects is to be aware of them while bringing myself back to my program. Could it be that easy?

"You're smiling," Carla says.

"I had a moment of clarity," I explain. "The more I hold onto things, the more miserable I'm destined to become."

"Really?" Carla's tone is a child's game of Go Fish, with tones of Hop Scotch and a dash of Hungry Hungry Hippo. "I've been trying to hold onto Tim, and that's clearly worked well."

I offer her my silliest Chutes and Ladders reply. "Obviously."

Then, we laugh—at the warped ways in which our minds work, the way intellect and emotion can completely diverge, and the insanity of refusing to let go.

"Isn't it funny?" Carla says. "Sometimes, the best way to move past adult problems is to apply the wisdom of Beginner's Mind."

Step Seven:

Humbly asked Him to remove our shortcomings. (Rabbit Pose)

42

"Hey, there. You heading home?" The voice belongs to the shadows.

I startle. "Who's that?"

It's 9:30. Well past sundown. The meeting ended thirty minutes ago. I shouldn't have stayed so long afterward, but I wanted to help put away the chairs, and April had been eager to get home and kiss the girls before they fell asleep, so I told her I didn't need her to stick around and walk out with me. Now, everyone is gone. I count five car lengths before I can duck, safely, inside my Hyundai and drive away.

As I rifle through my purse for my keys, the voice's owner steps out into the dim light of the only lamppost in this deserted church parking lot.

I see his handsome face and let out a relieved sigh. "Garrett –"

I've forgotten about him—mainly because I'm trying to become a different person.

"Simple question."

"What question?" I'm too rattled to remember the words he's only just spoken.

"You heading home?"

The moon illuminates his faint five o'clock shadow and strong, sinewy hands.

"Look, Garrett, I'm not interested, okay?" I try to sound convincing. "I've told you, I'm not dating."

His shirt stretches across the drum of his ribcage. He's been working out. I start to say something about April and sponsorship and the need for a year, but Garrett cuts me off before I have a chance to sever the chords of our connection with that magical incantation that has saved me once before.

My sponsor...

"Fuck, Jess, stop lying!"

"Excuse me?"

"I heard about you kissing Paul. And about Joshua."

"Who?"

"Joshua. The guy you took home and fucked a couple nights ago."

"Oh. I didn't know his name."

Joshua. I like the ring of it. It sounds like a boyfriend-material name. Much better than Rocko.

"Yeah. Bullshit you're not dating right now."

Garrett's body pins me against my car, every part of him hard. Words desert me—not that I really want to say anything. In this moment, his lips look full and kissable. I want to lean in and taste that angry snarl. To take him back to my apartment and tangle in my still-unwashed sheets until Monday night transitions into Tuesday morning. Maybe, this time, I'll cum. Maybe, this time, it'll fill me up, instead of emptying me out.

"You're a fucking slut," he says.

A rattling door. We both turn toward the sound, but it's just wind. No one is around to save me from my tendencies.

As Garrett reaches toward me, I see Dwight's hands—sure and strong and full of the kind of confidence I've never once possessed. For a moment, I'm enticed by the violence and cruelty and brutality of lust, then something in me whispers *Breathe* and a bucket of ice water douses my desire. I slap Garrett—hard—across the face and use the momentary window of his surprise to climb inside my car, slam and lock the door.

"Leave me alone!" I shout through the rolled-up glass.

"Fucking cunt!" Garrett shouts back.

With trembling fingers, I turn the key in the ignition, then, for the first time in my life, I flee from the touch of a man I'm attracted to.

43

February 28th. On the thirty-third anniversary of my birth, I awake feeling like death. The realization that I'm twenty-five days sober floods me with simultaneous regret at having screwed up and gratitude that I'm not drunk.

Seconds after my eyelids open, before I've even gotten out of bed, my phone rings. A number I recognize, but still haven't programmed into my phone—just in case.

"Hi, Mom."

"Jessica. I won't keep you long. Just calling to wish you a happy birthday and to tell you your gift should be arriving later."

"Thanks."

"Well, that's it, sweetheart. Like I said, I don't want to keep you."

Keep me? It's been all of fourteen seconds.

"Mom?"

"I hope I didn't wake you. I know it's early, and you probably sleep in, but I wanted to catch you while you were alert and let you know I love you."

"I love you, too."

A click—a temporary lapse in our connection.

"That's Chloe calling on the other line."

"I –"

"I should go, sweetheart. Your sister needs me. I'll tell her to call you after we're done. Happy thirty-third."

Dial tone. Emptiness. I crawl out from under the covers. Last night, awash in pre-birthday self-pity, I ate too much Ben & Jerry's. Still, a sugar hangover is better than the alcohol alternative.

I take a hot shower, dress in a new Old Navy outfit I bought on my coffee-shop-employee budget and head to the Free Café to start my shift. I'm still not back to full-time hours, and I could've taken today off, but I thought it best to stick with my typical routine.

"Like hey Jess! Like how are you?"

"Fine. You?"

Tina's nails are the color of day-old bruises and her lips remind me of blood. I wonder if, when my mother used to lecture me about my former fashion choices, she might've been onto something after all.

Mom. She couldn't get off the phone fast enough. Not that I blame her. Nevertheless, it hurts. I wonder what she and Chloe talk about—secret aspects of their lives that I'm not privy to.

Then again, there's a lot about me that neither of them know.

"A cappuccino and a cruller, please."

"Hey, Jimmy! How's it going?"

I haven't told anyone today's my birthday. Especially not April. She'd insist on celebrating, and I don't want to commemorate this day—only to endure it.

My cell rings. *Chloe?* No. It's him. Dwight. Calling to let me know he remembered. I can't pick up. To do so would knock over all my carefully arranged dominoes, so I force down the swell of longing in my heart and let my stepdad go to voicemail.

"One cruller coming right up."

"You okay?"

"I'm fine. A little tired."

"I like your outfit."

"Thanks."

"Special occasion?"

I shrug. "Just another day."

My shift sails by on a sea of customers, coworker small-talk and cups of scalding hot caffeine. When it's over, I say goodbye to Tina and head toward one of only two places where I'd be willing to spend this particular twenty-four.

I'll hit a meeting tomorrow night. Right now, there's something I'm craving more than my daily dose of AA.

The familiar VW. My teacher inside, lighting candles in the darkness. Rhonda's Thursday night Restore and Renewal.

I stand at the top of my mat, arms down by my sides, feet securely rooted to the floor.

"Can you feel grounded?" she inquires. "Really, truly rooted in what is, rather than on what you wish could be."

Thirty-three years of blown-out candles and wishes that refused to manifest.

This year, I won't have cake. I will have another day sober, and a silent, gentle inner opening as I move to music that inspires introspection.

In Downward Dog, Rhonda puts her hands on my spine, tracing each vertebra with her fingers as if I were Braille or, maybe, a flesh-and-bones connect-the-dots. I let myself let go—let the tension of expectation evaporate out of me. And, pretty soon, I'm in Shavasana, my home away from home.

When it's over, as I gather my belongings, Rhonda smiles at me from the front of the room. "Your practice is really coming along."

"Thanks. I love your classes."

"Well, I love having you, so keep coming back."

Fifteen minutes later, back at my building, I trudge up the stairs and in front of my apartment door is a bouquet of multicolored roses in a clear crystal vase. An upsurge of hope, dashed as soon as I read the words inscribed on the tiny card within.

To Jessica,

May you always remember that God is watching.

Love, Mom

Beside the vase rests a FedEx envelope. I tear it open. A check with my mother's name neatly inscribed on the signature line. Useful. Impersonal. Indicative of the distance in our relationship. She doesn't know me well enough to know what I might want or need, so she's outsourced the gift-buying to me.

I let myself in and call for a pizza. Just before it arrives, my cell phone pings with a text message.

Happy birthday, Chloe writes.

I respond—immediately and with gratitude. Thanks, sis. Miss you. How are you? It's been too long.

My words are carried out into the vortex. She doesn't reply.

≠ 44 ≠

A paunchy middle-aged woman with a wicked overbite and the kind of short helmet haircut that strips her of all traces of femininity sits at the front of the room.

"Thanks for asking me to share my story," she says.

I've opted for the Chestnut Hill Friday Night Women's Meeting tonight—opted to get away from Garrett and Paul and anyone else with a penis—not because I'm scared of men, but because I'm terrified of my own susceptibility.

I probably shouldn't have, but I listened to Dwight's voicemail this morning.

"Jesse, kiddo. How's it feel to be the big three-three? Call me, will you? There's a lot I want to say, but not on a machine. I love you though. And I miss you."

April knows something's up. Except for after Garrett, I've never been one to suggest a women-only environment.

"Did something happen?" she asked when I called her, earlier, to see if she'd meet me at the Church of the Nazarene instead of Our Lady of Mercy.

And, because I'm striving to be honest, I admitted that, yes, something did, but said I didn't want to talk about it.

"Remember, secrets keep us sick."

I gave in—partially—and told my sponsor about Joshua, but not about Garrett (His sickness is his own secret to share—or not), and about Dwight.

"Oh God, Jess! Why'd he call you?"

This led to telling her about my birthday.

"Why didn't you say anything?" she scolded. "I'd have thrown you a party or something."

"Which is why I didn't say anything."

"How are you feeling about him having call?"

"Unsafe."

"He wouldn't show up at your apartment, would he?"

How could I explain that the threat wasn't coming from him, but from my own pattern of relationship insanity?

At least, here, in this room full of women, I can be true to myself and my sobriety.

The stranger at the front runs her fingers through her barely existent hair and smiles toothily out at us. “I’m Charlene, and I’m a low-down, dirty drunk.”

“Hi Charlene,” we chorus.

She launches into her narrative.

“I had to learn about humility the hard way because I was the kinda person who thought my shit didn’t stink. That’s why, today, when I introduce myself at meetin’s, I always say right off that I’m a low-down, dirty drunk. I need to remind myself on a daily basis that, if not for the grace of my Higher Power, I’d be dead right now. I ain’t nothing without Him. Funny, ain’t it, ‘cause, back when I’se drinking, I thought I was too cool for God. I thought I’se too cool for everybody—includin’ the husband who’d divorced me, the kids who preferred to live with their dad, and the twelve bosses that fired me for being unreliable.”

A few of the old timers chuckle appreciatively while newer heads, like my own, nod along in recognition.

“When I came into these rooms, I was forty-two, broke as hell, jobless, my kids wouldn’t speak to me, and my ex-husband refused to return my calls. In case you can’t tell, I ain’t from here originally, but I moved up from Alabama to live in my parents’ basement, ‘cause I didn’t have a pot to piss in and I’d done burned damn near every other bridge I could think of. I was a grown-ass woman and my folks told me I could live with them on one condition. I had to go to at least one AA meetin’ a week. I thought them sons of bitches were crazy, but, wouldn’t you know it, AA don’ pissed in my cocktail.

“After I started comin’ here, alcohol stopped takin’ away my pain. Y’all understood me—much as I hated bein’ understood. You told me I was an egomaniac with an inferiority complex and that, deep down, I hated myself. I tried not to believe you, and, for a while, I kept drinking. I got sicker and sorrier than ever until, finally, one day, I figured *What the hell? Life can’t get any worse*, and I surrendered.

“I found a sponsor, sobered up, and started working the steps like my life depended on it—because it did. I was doin’ okay until I got to step six and realized I didn’t know how to get out of my own way. Sure, I might not’ve been drinking anymore, but I was still the same, ass-backward person I’d always been. Shit, I could hold onto a resentment” (She drags out the word *hold*, making it sound like h-o-o-o-o-l-l-l-l-d) “like nobody’s business. And I was the queen of self-pity.

Nothing was ever my fault or my responsibility. As far as I was concerned, life had done me dirty and everyone else needed to change.

"I was about a year and a half sober when I hit the worst emotional bottom I could imagine. I was so miserable I nearly went back to drinkin'. I wanted to. I sure as shit wanted somebody to take away the pain. But my ego wouldn't let me. It kept sayin', 'Charlene, you have a year and a half. If you pick up now, you'll be provin' your sorry sumbitch ex-husband right.' I can't tell you what happened, or how it happened, but I remember sittin' in a meetin' one day and realizin' that the reason I was still so fuckin' miserable wasn't because of anyone or anything else. It was because I was still doing what I wanted to do, not what my Higher Power wanted me to do. I hadn't surrendered. Not really."

I feel a sudden shock of pain and turn my attention to my fingers. Without realizing it, I've been picking at an errant cuticle and have gouged a chunk out of my flesh.

"So, I told my sponsor I was ready to work, and she told me to list all my character defects—pride, greed, selfishness, self-seekin', resentment, lust, gluttony, self-pity, and whatnot. Then, I got down on my knees and said the seventh step prayer over and over again. Only, instead of saying 'I pray that You now remove from me every *single* defect of character,' I don' listed my character defects one at a time. I asked God to take away my pride, my greed, my selfishness, my self-seekin', my resentment, my lust, my gluttony, my self-pity, and the like. And, I'm telling you, my Higher Power don' whitewashed my soul.

"Don't get me wrong. I'm still one lowdown sumabitch, but I started to see who God was, and who I was and, 'fore long, I found myself wantin' to let go of all my bullshit. I mean, who wouldn't wanna surrender the worst parts of themselves to someone who loves them more'n they can even comprehend?"

When Charlene stops sharing, I raise my bleeding hand and thank her. "Your words made me realize there's something I have to do before I can fully surrender."

April gives me a sideways glance, no doubt wondering what epiphany I've achieved in this room I never would've sought out if not for the consequences of my own character defects. I'll tell her, of course, when the time is right, what I need to do and why. In the meantime, I'm awash in recognition at the power of this stranger's share. It wasn't just her words that touched me, but the way she'd been able to rebuild a life after losing everything.

Charlene rewards my disclosure with a big toothy grin and nods her practically hairless head and, for the moment anyway, she and I are exactly the same.

≠ 45 ≠

I arrive in a simple black dress, a pair of bangle earrings, and the faintest touch of lip-gloss, applied as an afterthought in case I run into anyone who might look at me long enough to notice. I know coming here today, when I'm not ready to face her, I'm taking a risk. But how can I move forward if I don't dismantle the idols of my past?

Never mind that the first service doesn't start until ten, her car's already in the parking lot. She'll have been inside since nine.

Whenever Chloe and I used to complain about how dumb it was that she made us get to church an hour early, Mom would say, "Give God this lifetime, and He'll give you an eternity."

But I'm grown-up now. So, I skip the before-church "hellos" and "I'll pray for yous" and "we haven't seen you since you were this bigs," slip in unnoticed a few minutes before the service starts, and slump down in a pew in the back, where no one except the other stragglers will see me.

The priest of my childhood has been replaced by a new one. At first glance, the man at the altar appears to be the same one who conducted my Communion, but time hasn't stood still. In the eighteen years since I was last here, the seventy-year-old white guy in robes I remember has died (and, ostensibly, gone to heaven) and been succeeded by another seventy-year-old equally white guy in equally antiquated robes.

The altar boys seem the same too. But they're the sons of the now-men I watched hold the books and ring the bells. The men I went to school with and who refused to associate with me lest I contaminate them with my wellspring of sinfulness.

The only things that remain untouched are the stained glass windows hovering above the altar. My favorite one has always been the image of Jesus—arms outstretched like wings.

When Mom and Dad first started taking Chloe and me here, I told them it felt like God's son was giving me a hug. I didn't understand about bloody palms and betrayal, and Daddy didn't explain. Instead, he told me that Jesus hugged everyone.

"God is love, Jesse," he said. "Don't ever let anyone tell you otherwise."

I stand and kneel and sing and cross myself at all the right times, but it's hard to focus on the service while watching my mother's stoic shoulders from behind.

Mom's glossy hair, blonder and longer and shiner than mine, still reminds me of Rapunzel's. She deserves a fairytale ending. Instead, her princes—charming, cruel, and cunning—have reneged on their promises of rescue.

Dwight is the second husband Mom's lost, and the idea of her being locked up in the tower of loneliness sends me down a rabbit hole of remorse.

I should never have been with him.

I should've been a better daughter.

I should've respected what they had.

I should've loved her more—and hated myself less.

As the priest rambles on about the redemptive power of God's love and the importance of doing unto others, my mind flits like fireflies from the past to the present to the future.

"Our Father, who art in heaven, hallowed be thy Name, thy kingdom come, thy will be done, on earth as it is in heaven. Give us this day our daily bread. And forgive us our trespasses, as we forgive those who trespass against us. And lead us not into temptation, but deliver us from evil. For thine is the kingdom, and the power, and the glory, for ever and ever. Amen."

The congregants stand in union, ready to stride penitently to the altar and ingest bread and wine in memory of sacrificial love. I stand too. Only, as they head toward the front, I slip out the back. It wouldn't feel right to partake in such a sacred ritual. Besides, how would I navigate the wine? If I eat Christ's body, but refuse to drink his blood, does that mean I'll only be half saved?

On Shrove Tuesday, I join the bored, ungrateful housewives in line at the confessional. These women—every inch of them painted and waxed and shellacked to perfection—filter in and out of the tiny sin booth and admit to yelling at their husbands, catching their kids masturbating, and fantasizing about doing unspeakable things to the gardener while I wait in the shadow of Jesus' open arms to divulge transgressions that might actually render me unworthy of a Higher Power's love.

I wonder if the priest gets bored with these women and their insignificant sins. Or maybe they have more sinister secrets than I imagine. Secrets like the ones I hide behind my own fabricated smile.

When it's my turn, I enter and kneel. "Forgive me, Father, for I have sinned. It's been eighteen years since my last confession."

He says nothing.

I take a deep breath, then forge ahead. "When I was five, I wished my dad would die, then he died. I once accidentally hit a cat with my car and killed it."

He waits.

"From age fifteen to just before I turned eighteen, I engaged in a sexual relationship with my stepdad. At seventeen, I had an abortion. And, from the time I was fifteen up until this year, I've lived my life as an addict and alcoholic."

He lets the silence drift between us like a lost balloon. I guess he senses I have more to say.

"I've had a lot of indiscriminate sex, and I've hurt a lot of people—including myself. I've tried to commit suicide, which I know is a sin. I'm broken, Father."

When the priest finally replies, what he says is kinder than I expect. "We're all broken in the eyes of God. And we're all loved, not in spite of our sinful natures, but because of them." He instructs me to say five *Our Fathers* and six *Hail Marys'*.

"Is that all? Then, I'll be forgiven."

"By God, yes. I'll pray that you can forgive yourself."

"Thank you, Father."

As I rise to exit the confessional, the priest adds one last piece of advice. "My child, we are each only responsible for our own sins, not the sins of our fathers—or stepfathers. God doesn't reside in shame, and neither should you. Now, go and sin no more."

I'm not naïve enough to believe that another human being can absolve me of my past. And, if there is a God, I'm sure he doesn't confine himself to churches. Yet, on my knees, saying my *Hail Marys'*, the ice around my heart begins to thaw.

> "Hail Mary, full of grace. The Lord is with thee.
> Blessed art thou amongst women,
> and blessed is the fruit of thy womb, Jesus.
> Holy Mary, Mother of God,
> pray for us sinners,
> now and at the hour of our death. Amen."

Eighteen years since I've said those words, yet they are as familiar as a mother's bedtime lullaby.

> Hush little baby don't say a word.

Papa's gonna buy you a mockingbird...

And as comforting.

As the nightlight of forgiveness illuminates my soul, the monsters scatter from beneath the bed, just as they did when I was younger and my mother sat with me after a nightmare.

"It's okay, beautiful. God is bigger than any monsters, and he's watching over you."

The others have performed their contrition and left to go home to their Main Line houses, husbands, and 2.5 children, but I'm not ready to leave the site of my newfound salvation, so I walk around the churchyard and find a wrought-iron bench from which to call Carla.

"Hey, do you have a minute?"

"Sure. I was just throwing out all the toiletries and other stuff Tim left behind."

"How's it going?"

"It's not as painful as it would've been a couple months ago."

"But still more painful than you'd like it to be?"

"Isn't everything? So, what's up with you?"

"I just went to confession for the first time in eighteen years." I don't share the specific nature of my sins, but I explain that I grew up Catholic and that I've been feeling like I needed to share some things with a priest.

"So...?" Carla wants to know. "What does that *mean*?"

"I don't think it means anything. I'm certainly not going to return to Catholicism. It's not my path."

My path is on my yoga mat, one breath and one moment at a time. Still, it feels good to have dusted off my religious resentment and repaired an old spiritual rift. I'm realizing that I have to make peace with a God outside myself before I can find a Higher Power within.

"Well, I think it's pretty great that you're working so hard on your sobriety, and, if it made you feel better to get stuff out, I say good for you."

And it is good. It is better. Not all better. Not magic.

Like Carla, with Tim, my pain is slowly dissipating. There's still a lot I wish I could change about myself—still a lot of damage to undo. But, for what it's worth, I feel ready to take the seventh step.

≠ 46 ≠

"Sure, you can use the room."

"By myself? For an hour?"

It's after Rhonda's Wednesday afternoon Easy Flow class. I've waited for everyone to filter out so I can make my request beneath the shade of the painted Tree of Life.

"Of course. If that's what you need." Rhonda thinks for a minute. "How about Saturday morning at 7:45? You can have the room before my 9:00 Vinyasa class. Will that work?"

I hug her. "That's perfect. Thank you."

On Saturday morning, I arrive at 7:30, my yoga mat slung over one shoulder, a small canvas knapsack over the other. I've packed a candle, a lighter, my step-journal, three pens (in case any of them run out of ink), a Deva Premal CD, and a copy of my AA *Big Book*.

Rhonda's bright yellow VW is already here, and all the studio lights are on, but my teacher looks tired when she opens the door. "Long night."

"Thanks for letting me in."

"Thank *you* for letting me in. From what you've told me, your spiritual practice sounds profound."

I haven't given Rhonda any details. I simply explained that my spiritual mentor wanted me to spend an hour in reverent worship and asked if I could use the space at Branches for an hour.

"Yeah," I agree. "I'm lucky."

"I wish I had a spiritual mentor." Rhonda looks as if she wants to say more.

"Is everything okay?"

"Oh, yeah. Just exhausted. You need anything?"

"Um… Can you show me how to work the sound system?"

She walks me through the process of synching the CD player with the surround sound. "I'm gonna go get a cup of coffee and a bagel. Are you okay if I lock the exterior door and leave you here alone?"

"Absolutely. Thank you, again."

"Need anything? Food? Coffee? A frappe mocha something or other?"

"No thanks. I'm okay."

This is one of the few times my teacher and I have spoken about anything other than yoga, and I'm struck by the sudden realization that I've never thought about her doing any of the normal stuff—eating, drinking, sleeping, and the like.

It's 7:39 when I hear the main studio door open and close.

I'm alone. Deval Premal's voice surrounds me. I stand at the top of my mat, raise my eyes skyward, and begin to flow through a series of reverent Sun Salutations.

Tadasana, Urdhva Hastasana, Uttanasana, Ardha Uttanasana, Chaturanga Dandasana, Urdhva Mukha Svanasana, Adho Mukha Svanasana, Ardha Uttanasana, Uttanasana, Urdhva Hastasana, Tadasana.

As soon as I find my rhythm, I elaborate on the beautiful simplicity of the standard vinyasa by adding a Warrior I here, a Radiant Warrior there, transitioning from Dancer's to Triangle, to Crescent, to Pigeon. Then, I unwind the sequence, like a string of rosary beads, reversing the order until time folds in on itself.

As I move, I pray out loud, as April has instructed.

"My Creator, I am now willing that You should have all of me, good and bad. I pray that You now remove from me every single defect of character which stands in the way of my usefulness to You and my fellows. Grant me strength, as I go out from here, to do Your bidding. Amen."

I repeat the prayer over and over again while my body performs its own reverent ritual.

Mountain, Upward Salute, Standing Forward Fold, Half Forward Bend, Plank, Upward Dog, Downward Dog, Half Forward Bend, Standing Forward Fold, Upward Salute, Mountain.

So many elements coalescing.

Body. Mind. Spirit. Breath. Prayer.

Inhale. Exhale. Move. Flow.

Stillness.

After what feels like forever and no time at all, I slump into Child's Pose and continue to implore a God I'm just beginning to believe in to remove my entrenched defective patterns. I list my character defects, one at a time, like Charlene's sponsor had her do.

"Please..." I picture a man in the sky with kind eyes, a broad, inviting smile, and a single wave of white in his mass of dark hair. "Take away my pride..."

When my prayers have vacuumed out my insides, stripping me of the dust and the distractions that have been getting in the way of any spiritual connection with a power greater than myself, I sit in the flickering candlelight and write a letter to my father. What I write isn't so much for him, whose love for me has never wavered, but for my own skeptical, sacrilegious heart.

By the time I hear the outside door open and close, fifty-five minutes after I've begun, I know that something is different, and part of me is excited to see what will happen next.

47

The day I moved out was exhilarating and terrifying. Like jumping out of a plane. Only, I didn't have a parachute. I was eighteen—too old to be his little girl anymore, too young to make a major life decision. Still, I understood that, the second I showed Dwight our tape, there would be no coming home again. You don't break up with—and blackmail—someone, then slink back a week later, say "my bad" and expect it all to be okay.

Mom didn't fight my decision to leave. I didn't realize I wanted her to until she made it clear that she wasn't sorry to see me go. Not that I blamed her. I came and went at all hours of the day and night, got caught with random men—even after Bruce—and always refused to apologize.

"I'm glad you're growing up, Jessica. Of course, we're here if you need us." Mom said as she handed me a wad of cash, which telegraphed the message *But please don't take me up on my offer. I really don't want to deal with you.*

Dwight was far more affected by my decision. Then again, for Mom, me walking out was nothing more than a child growing up and moving on. For him, it was a break-up. And a bad one.

Despite the boldness of my exit, I wasn't equipped to deal with life on my own. Not that I was completely on my own. I moved in with a pot-dealer. Ben and I had been seeing each other for a few months. He was a tall, gangly intellectual who smoked more of his product than he sold. He lived in a basement apartment in Spring Garden, just a short subway ride from Temple, where I'd enrolled and where he hung out on the quad conducting his dime bag transactions and philosophizing with the psychology undergrads. I liked him.

He never asked questions about why, when my mother and sister went to the Poconos for Chloe's youth group retreat, I chose to stay home with my stepdad instead of crashing at his place. Or why I showed up at his door with a suitcase and declared that I could never go home again. Ben and I never talked about anything substantial. We simply had fun. Until reality intruded.

A few unpaid bills, and disconnected utilities, later, I got my own place in a sketchy section of South Philly. So what if my apartment was smaller than my walk-in closet in the house I grew up in? I was independent. I was responsible. I was holding it together—for a while anyway.

In the beginning, I went to college part-time, worked part-time in a lawyer's office, and confined my drinking and using to after five and on weekends. Granted, my boss seemed more interested in the length of my skirts than my thoughts about the law, but he never said anything when I came into work hung-over or did homework at my desk, so I was okay with our arrangement.

The nights were the hardest. My neighborhood wasn't the kind of place where a single white woman had any business being after dark. I never left my apartment without a can of mace, and I always made sure that whatever guy I was screwing at the time walked me all the way to my front door before heading home to his wife or girlfriend.

I open my eyes. I've been sitting here in Staff Pose on my kitchen floor since eleven. Sleep eludes me, so I'm trying to distract myself with yoga. It isn't working.

Ironically, despite my abstemiousness, I feel as aimless now as I did in the days after I deserted Dwight. I'm still working part-time at a job where nobody cares what I'm thinking, and I'm still taking classes—just a different kind than before. The only real change between where I am now and where I used to be is that, these days, when I wake up, I can remember what I did the previous night. Still, discontentment nags at me. There's more to life than twelve step meetings, step work, and some crappy, low-level job. There has to be.

The old me would've dealt with my current self-actualization crisis by getting high, or hooking up. Instead, I get in my Hyundai and head down to Forbidden Drive. Who cares if it's close to midnight (not an ideal hour for an unarmed blue-eyed, blonde-haired, one-hundred-twenty pound white girl to be wandering around alone)? I'm okay with this version of living on *the edge*.

I don my headphones and scroll through my IPod to my sobriety playlist: *Starting Over* by Macklemore, *Rehab* by the died-of-alcohol poisoning Amy Winehouse, Pink's *Sober* and the song by the same name by a very different artist—Selena Gomez...

I walk for hours—away from the life I once knew and the person I'm trying not to be anymore, although, toward what, I'm not sure.

It's not until the Monday morning sun caresses the horizon that I finally drag myself, exhausted home. I still have no more clarity than before, but at least I've wandered long enough that my mind will grant me a reprieve. I close the blinds on the misty hue of dawn and drift into a daytime slumber. But not before first voicing a single, fervent prayer.

"Father, God, please show me my next step."

My words linger in the air like a lullaby.

Step Eight:

Made a list of all persons we had harmed, and became willing to make amends to them all. (Tree Pose)

48

Like fuzzy up-bubbles, rising to the top of a shaken soda, memories surface. In yoga, in meditation, as I go about my day, and even in my dreams, they rush up within me, unignorable in their intensity. I used to see these memories as a bad thing, until Rhonda and April offered a different interpretation.

My yoga teacher says that the physical discipline of yoga offers opportunities to revisit our pasts through the lenses of our presents so we can be free of old shackles. April uses AA language. She tells me I'm letting go of *the bondage of self*.

To me, it feels more significant that simply breaking out of chains. I'm also reclaiming good things. This morning, as I was brushing my teeth, I remembered coming home from pre-school and announcing I was ready for my first loose tooth to come out.

"The tooth fairy is gonna leave me money!" I declared. "Five whole dollars!" As if the amount were a foregone conclusion.

"Really?" Mommy smirked.

"Yes! You'll see." I was confident at first, but, after days' worth of wiggling yielded no results, I grew dispirited. "It'll never happen! I'm doomed!" Even at four, I had a talent for melodrama.

Mommy looked at Daddy, who laughed and asked if I wanted help.

I glared at him like he was an idiot. Hadn't he heard me bemoaning my lack of loose-tooth fortune for *days*? If he'd had a solution, he should've intervened immediately and not made me wait.

Daddy explained the procedure. Mommy—his skeptical, and reluctant, helpmate—retrieved the floss.

"You sure?" she asked.

"Don't be such a worrier, Evangeline. It'll be fine. Promise."

Daddy tied a thin Oral-B noose around my tooth, then secured the other end to the doorknob. Although I tried not to be scared, I kept inching closer and closer to the door, bracing myself for its inevitable slam.

"One!" Daddy bellowed. "Two!"

On "Three!" he slammed the door.

Nothing happened. There was too much slack in the line.

"It didn't work!" I took a giant, petulant, step backward, and my tooth catapulted across the room.

That night, the tooth fairy exceeded my four-year-old expectations by leaving five dollars under my pillow and something else too—a tiny, gold-shaped charm for the delicate gold bracelet that is now too small for my grown-up wrists. I kept that bracelet, even after selling so much else. It's tucked away in my top dresser drawer, behind my socks.

"You were smiling in Shavasana." Beside me, Carla rolls up her mat.

We've just finished the Saturday afternoon Easy Flow Class.

"Weirdo. Why were you looking at me in Shavasana?"

She shakes her head. "Honestly, Jess, you seem different lately. Happier and more solid."

I start to protest, then realize that she's right. I'm not sure how or when it happened, but I'm changing. Forty-one days sober and not nearly as haunted by the past. In fact, some of it, as painful as it was at the time, was actually kind of funny.

One weekend, when Chloe and I were teenagers, Mom and Dwight took a trip to a B&B in Maryland to "rekindle their romance" and left my sister and me at home. Well, left *me* at home. Chloe opted to stay at her best friend's house, which I told myself was what I wanted too. That way, I could have people over without worrying about her tattling. So, why the churning sludge of shame at knowing that the sister who'd once admired and emulated me had traded her idolization for aversion and would now rather be anywhere than with me?

"Don't invite anyone over," Dwight ordered as he headed out the door, dragging Mom's suitcase behind him because it was too heavy to heft with his bad back.

I gave him the finger, then sprinted up the stairs. I'd been pissed at him all week. He'd never taken *me* to a B&B. He never did *anything* romantic for *me*.

"She's my wife," he kept saying—as if I needed the reminder. "Stop acting so childish."

But I *was* a child. I was entitled to be petulant.

"I mean it, Jesse!" he shouted as I barged past my mother on her way down the stairs.

Fuck them both. I'd do what I wanted.

What I wanted wasn't to have more than fifty people over. True, I asked a guy I was crushing on, one of my girl friends, and the dude she'd been seeing, to hang out at my place, but my plan was to get drunk, and high, listen to music, and revenge-fuck my crush while, somewhere in Princess Anne, Dwight was making sweet, married, love to my mother.

But my friend told another friend, her guy told another guy, my crush told his crush, and so on and so forth until the house was full. Not just inside either. There were people everywhere.

"Hey! This is awesome!" someone shouted.

I looked out the window and saw three guys from my math class sitting on our roof, drinking, while a couple of girls whose names I didn't know looked up at them from where they were smoking cigarettes—and snuffing their butts out—on our lawn. Following their sightlines to the roof-boys, I noticed that my mother's white, flower-festooned, rose trellis was leaning slightly to the left. Shit. Now, I'd have to figure out how to keep it from coming unhinged. Or I could feign ignorance and hope Mom blamed the weather. I thought about kicking everyone out, but it was only Friday and my parental units weren't due back until Sunday. If I spent all of Saturday cleaning, they'd never know what I'd done.

It wouldn't be the first time I'd thrown a party without getting caught. Only, a pipe burst at the B&B. The proprietors were really apologetic and offered all the guests the option to stay or leave. Not wanting to deal with construction noises on what was supposed to be their romantic weekend, Mom and Dwight opted to come home early.

It was stupid, really. I'd heard the phone ringing several times throughout the day, but I was too intoxicated, and too intent on making out with my crush, and making sure that bitch Taylor Marson didn't get her perfectly manicured hands on him, to pick up. I couldn't figure out why the guy I liked was into Taylor anyway. Probably because she was a virgin and he had some dumbass delusion of being her first. Whatever. What I lacked in innocence, I made up for in experience.

I should've answered. Mom was trying to reach me to let me know about her and Dwight's early return. Instead, my mother and my lover returned to a house full of drunk teenagers and me half-naked on their bed with some random who didn't even go to my school. As it turned out, my crush hooked up with Taylor after all, although I heard he didn't get past second-base. It wasn't my fault. I *had* to use Mom and Dwight's room. My girl friend and her guy were in my room—a sock on the doorknob a clear, unbreachable signal to stay the hell away.

"Young lady!" Mom swung open her bedroom door. "You are in so much trouble!"

My stepdad/lover stood, arms across his chest, radiating rage.

"You really should've answered the phone," Mom said.

I was so high, I misunderstood. "Hello." I picked up their bedside receiver. "Hello? Hello!" I stared, blank facedly, at my mother and her husband. "No one's there." Realization dawned. "*Oh. I get it!* You meant before." I started laughing.

Mom and Dwight were not amused, so I turned toward my make-out buddy, to share the moment with someone I hoped would join in the joke, but he'd already fled.

"It's not funny, Jesse! You are in so much trouble!"

"Screw both of you!" I fled down the hall and banged on my bedroom door until my friend and her guy emerged, rumpled, took in what had happened, and scurried past me down the stairs.

While Mom and Dwight kicked out all the guests, I locked my bedroom door behind me, stripped down to my underwear, and climbed beneath my sheets.

Fifteen minutes later, Dwight was pounding on my door. "Open up! We need to talk about this!"

"Leave me alone!" I shouted back. "You don't want to hear what I have to say!"

I guess he figured it was better not to stand, shouting, outside my closed wooden door—lest I let out any full-volume truths.

"This isn't over!"

"Fuck you, Mr. B&B!"

I listened as his footsteps receded down the hall, then flopped back down and passed out.

The next morning, I woke to the smell of fried bacon, scrambled eggs, and something freshly baked. Muffins? Bread? Coffee cake? Too bad I never found out.

My stomach growling, partly with its typical a.m. hunger, partly with the post-pot munchies, I leapt out of bed and sprinted down the stairs. "That smells delicious!" In the kitchen, I grabbed a banana out of the fruit bowl.

"*You*!" Mom brandished her spatula. "Are in big trouble, young lady!"

"Shit. Last night wasn't a dream?"

"No, Jessica, it wasn't. Honestly, living with you feels like a nightmare."

On my way back to my room to await a punishment I knew I wouldn't obey, I snagged a piece of bacon from the serving plate on the table.

"You know," I tell Carla as I stuff my own mat into its convenient container, "I feel happier. How about you?"

"As much as I hate to admit it, it's easier now that Tim's out of the house."

That's the thing about letting go. As frightening as it is, it can also be freeing, which is why, as painful as it is to think about, I understand Chloe's decision to let go of me.

The night before my sister turned twenty-one, she called to remind me—again—that she was having a party. I didn't need the reminder. When she phoned, I was halfway through wrapping her present—a bottle of Gran Patrón Platinum. A month before, when she'd asked me to come, I'd been surprised, and flattered, that she wanted me there.

"It's a small dinner thing, Jesse," she told me after I'd promised to be there, and again on the phone as I wrapped her top-shelf tequila. Five of her closest friends and I—her big sister—were invited to celebrate Chloe's entry into legality. "It's important that you make it."

"I'll be there," I told her.

How irresponsible did she think I was?

"And be on time. 7:30 means 7:30, not 8:30 or nine."

What a condescending bitch! Chloe was my *little* sister. She had no right to talk to me like I was a two-year-old.

"You don't need to remind me."

"Sorry. It's just that it's important."

"I know, Chloe. You act like I'm a fucking failure."

"I didn't mean –"

"It's okay. I'll see you at *7:30* tomorrow."

After we hung up, I opened her bottle. The tequila went down easy. The blackout that followed lasted two days. When I finally came to, I was in a holding cell in Roxborough. I'd been arrested for indecent exposure.

Luckily, the DA decided not to press charges and the cops let me out with a warning.

"You seem like a nice young woman," they told me. "But it doesn't matter how drunk you are, you're not allowed to urinate in public."

I promised to be more discerning about when and where I emptied my bladder then practically levitated out of jail, buoyed by having escaped the consequences of my literally piss-poor choices. It wasn't until I was walking down the street that I realized that my sister's birthday had come and gone and I'd been a no-show after all.

"What'd I say?"

"Huh?"

Carla and I are the only two left in the studio. "You look sad now."

"I'm just thinking about how much the people we love can hurt us and realizing that my sponsor's right. It's time to undo the damage I've caused."

≠ 49 ≠

Step eight: Made a list of all persons we had harmed, and became willing to make amends to them all.

I take my eighth-step list directly from my fourth step. 172 distinct individuals, some of whose names I don't even know. In those cases, I've written a description.

Guy with green eyes whose weed I stole at club...

Girl whose boyfriend I slept with...

I'm glad I kept my fourth-step list. Some people burn theirs and have to start over when making their amends inventory. I hate the idea of starting from scratch. As it is, I've had to add a few names that didn't make it onto my fourth step—customers from work, the nail-obsessed Tina, with whom I've been repeatedly sarcastic, some fellow AAers, and telephone solicitors.

Let's face it, even sober, I can be a bitch.

Because I kept my original inventory, the list isn't the hard part. The hard part is figuring out how to atone for what I've done.

"I don't know where to start," I tell April.

"Start with the most important person. That's where you'll experience the greatest healing."

But I'm paralyzed by the first name on my list.

"If I tell her, she'll hate me."

April instructs me—again—to read steps eight and nine.

"I've read them a bazillion times. They say we're not supposed to make amends if it'll hurt the other person."

"That mostly applies when it'd ruin a marriage, or get someone in legal trouble, or violate someone else's right to privacy."

"But that's *exactly* what's happening here. This'll ruin my mom's marriage."

"You mean the marriage that her cheating soon-to-be-ex has told you there's no hope of salvaging?"

I stick out my bottom lip—a gesture my sponsor can't see through the phone.

"Eight and nine," she says again, then hangs up on me.

As I sit at my kitchen table, a cup of coffee in one hand, my list in the other, my AA *Twelve & Twelve* open to page 77, I can't help but think back to when I was six.

I was on the jungle gym at Ashbridge Memorial Park when some snot-nosed brat hauled off and hit me. Okay, the assault wasn't entirely unprovoked. I'd tried to kiss him. But the boy could've said "no." He didn't have to punch me in the face.

"Girls have cooties!" my rejector shouted before running away from me, toward his oblivious—and, ostensibly, cootie-having—mother.

When my own mother saw me crying, she rushed over and scooped me into her arms. "What happened, Jessica?"

I recounted my experience while she kissed away my tears. Then, still holding me like a groom carrying his bride over a threshold, Mom stormed across the playground to confront my assailant. "You little bully!" she railed. "Apologize to my daughter this instant!"

I'd never heard my quiet, Christian mother scream before. Well, never at anyone but me.

Even when the boy started blubbering, Mom had zero pity. She turned her wrath toward his mother. "If you were paying attention to your son, instead of reading that trashy tabloid, he wouldn't have hit my daughter! What kind of mother are you? Do your *job*!"

Too stunned to be offended, the other woman stammered, "I'm sorry," then instructed her son to do the same. Of course, Mom forgave them. It was part of the Christian code of conduct. Turn the other cheek and all that.

"I love you, Mommy," I said when it was just the two of us again.

"I love you too, Jessica."

Mom and I spent the rest of the afternoon sliding down the slide, playing on the seesaw, and pushing each other on the swings. During one especially ardent underdog, I remember thinking she'd always protect me from mean boys. I didn't know then that, like the negligent, *Enquirer*-reading mother, the woman who gave me life would also avert her eyes at the wrong time, thereby enabling her own child to misbehave.

I want to tell my mother the truth, so I can stop harboring the belief that, if she really knew me, she wouldn't love me. But I don't want to tell her because, well, if she really knew me, she wouldn't love me.

"She has a right to know," April says. "Maybe not the details, but the fact that her husband isn't the man she thinks he is."

I let this soak in. Or try to.

"Besides," my sponsor continues, "what if, on some level, she already knows?"

April has just articulated my greatest fear.

"If she knew..." I can't complete the sentence. Some things really are unforgiveable.

"Just own your part. That's all you can do."

My part...

I don't even know what that is anymore.

≠ 50 ≠

Mom picks up on the first ring. "Jessica! Did he change his mind? Is he coming home?"

It hurts that, even when she sees my name, *he* is her first thought. But I try to be grateful that I'm still stored in her phone—still one of her contacts, even if we almost never reach out to one another.

"No, Mom. He hasn't. I'm sorry."

"Oh." I can feel the wind rushing out of her, like a balloon that someone let go without first tying off. I picture my mother dissolving on the floor, wilted and wrinkled, and impotent as rubber. But she doesn't dissolve—ever. Maybe, if she did, it would be easier to understand each other.

I'm the first to break the silence. "Hey, Mom?"

"Yes, honey."

"Thank you for the flowers and the check."

"Oh, Jessica, of course. I hope you bought yourself something nice."

"I'm sorry about Thanksgiving."

She chuckles softly to herself. "Turkey is overrated."

"I miss you."

"I miss you too, sweetie."

"Can I take you to lunch? Or dinner? Treat you to a cup of coffee? I'd really like to talk."

She hesitates. "Jessica, I don't know how to say this. You're my daughter, and I love you, but seeing you... On the phone, I can pretend you're not drunk, or high, or living with some *boyfriend* who beats you up, but, in person –"

"One boyfriend. One time."

That's not strictly true, but Mom only knows about Shayne, who sent me into traction during an impassioned argument. What she doesn't know is why. He caught me in bed with his brother.

"Jessica," Mom continues, "I know I put on a brave face, but seeing you with bruises and bags under your eyes looking like a... junkie... is difficult for me."

"I'm sober, Mom. I have been for a month and a half now. Before that, I actually managed to put together six months. I'm really trying to change."

It's as if I've just brought home a finger painting for the fridge, or a lopsided art class ashtray. No matter how inept an offering it is, my mother wants, proudly, to display the gift I've given her.

"Thank you, Jesus! Wait 'til I tell your sister!"

"I'm just hoping we can share a meal, or a nonalcoholic beverage, and start over."

We agree to meet for lunch in Center City at Chloe—Mom's favorite restaurant, the name of which I find ironic.

"It's BYOB," she tells me. "They don't serve alcohol."

"Thank you. That's thoughtful."

"I've been praying for this, Jessica."

"Me too, Mom. I've been praying too."

As we hang up, I picture her doing the sign of the cross.

Step Nine:

Made direct amends to such people wherever possible, except when to do so would injure them or others. (Feathered Peacock Pose)

≠ 51 ≠

Chloe is the epitome of elegance—exactly what I'd expect from a restaurant with the same name as my sister. In jeans and a peasant blouse, I'm clearly underdressed. But none of my old club clothes fit now that I'm no longer doing coke, and I can't afford new ones on my coffee-shop and partial-disability salary.

I'd planned to get off government subsidization completely, but, after my not too distant relapse, my doctor wants me to wait a little longer before returning to work full-time.

"Recovery is your job," he said.

So, here I am, ready to do the work sobriety requires.

"Jessica!" Mom is immaculately dressed in a Dolce & Gabbana pantsuit and holding a Chanel clutch. She doesn't comment on my inadequate outfit or clogged pores. "This is exactly what I've been hoping for."

You haven't heard what I'm here to tell you.

After the hostess shows us to our table, I open my menu and flinch.

Mom waves away my concern. "You're not treating me. So, don't worry about the prices."

"Are you sure?"

"Don't be silly."

"Thank you." Even without alcohol, this lunch would've set me back a week's pay.

"Let's indulge. We're celebrating."

"Are we?"

"Well, sure. There's a lot to be sad about right now, but you being sober is enough to make me forget all that—temporarily anyway. What do you say to a shared appetizer? The hors d'oeuvres here are incredible."

When Daddy was alive, we ate chips straight from the bag—licking our salty fingers before and after reaching in. Sure, we had money. Mom has always had money, even before she married Daddy. But he kept her grounded. Between the cash and the Catholicism, my mother has become practiced at shellacking over all her sorrow. But I don't buy her happy act. I know what lies buried within the graveyard of her grief.

"Whatever you want, Mom. I'm just glad you said yes to this."

"How could I not? You're my little girl. I don't know why you've felt a need to be so difficult all these years. Dwight and I hoped you'd come around."

"Can you not lump him in with you?"

When the waitress returns with her notepad, I let Mom order for both of us. She's better at making decisions.

Mom waits until the stranger walks away before disagreeing with me. In my family, we don't air our filthy laundry unless we're sure we're out of sight. "Dwight loves you like a father, Jessica. Just because he and I can't make it work doesn't mean –"

"Mom, I want to tell you something."

She takes a sip of her water. Her blonde hair is shiny. Mine is dry. The ends are split. Once upon a time, people told me I looked like her. Now, Chloe is her spitting image, and I'm nothing more than a badly-made replica.

"First, Jessica, let me congratulate you. Getting sober is quite the accomplishment. I've spoken to our priest, and he says –"

"Your priest? Mom, you know I'm not Catholic anymore."

Why do I feel a need to be confrontational? I'm here to apologize. Yet, the old me can't keep from seeping through the cracks.

"I wish you'd reconsider that, too. Anyway, the point is, I understand now that addiction is a disease and I want to apologize for judging your sickness instead of getting you the help you so clearly needed."

"I wouldn't have accepted it. I had to hit bottom and become ready on my own."

She nods. The appetizers come—lobster salad canapés and caramelized onion tartlets. Even though I've been eating foie gras and caviar since I was five, I feel like an imposter in my Free People blouse and thrift-shop jeans.

Nevertheless, I put on my best *Pretty Woman* smile and let the lobster linger on my tongue.

Mom attempts awkward small-talk. "Hasn't the weather been beautiful lately? Unseasonably warm for mid-March."

"Yeah."

She proceeds to denser subjects. "Did you know that your old friend Bruce and his wife are having another baby?"

"I haven't talked to Bruce since high school."

"Well, he has the sweetest family. I'm not sure what happened between you two, but he was a sweet boy."

Who climbed out my window after you caught me giving him a BJ.

"Are you seeing anyone, sweetheart?"

"Not right now. I'm pretty damaged when it comes to men."

Our salads arrive.

"I know. Because of your father. Honestly, I don't understand why his death left you so wounded while Chloe is so... well-adjusted." She spears a bite of arugula. Chews. "Dwight and I would sometimes speculate. He thought it was because you were older than she was when your father died. Do you think that could be it?"

"I think it's because of how young I was when I had sex for the first time—and of who I had it with."

"Oh, Jessica, do I really want to hear this?"

"No, Mom, but I have to tell you."

She sighs. More water.

"I was fifteen."

"Jessica!" She gazes up at the ceiling—finding it easier to implore her Lord for answers than to face me and my truth head-on.

"And the man was –" I take a sip of my own water, dousing the inner fire of self-judgment, and force myself to deliver the secret that makes me irredeemable. "Dwight."

"Excuse me?"

"I lost my virginity to Dwight, Mom."

The waitress delivers our snapper to the table, but neither Mom nor I make a move for our forks.

"But he was your... My... We... You were how old?"

"Fifteen when it started. It went on until just before my eighteenth birthday."

"Why didn't you tell me?" She holds her glass of water in front of her heart, like a shield.

I'm careful to choose the least wounding words I can think of. "I was ashamed."

She puts the glass down, assured, I suppose, that the only attack she'll be required to endure will be the one she perpetrates against herself. "How could I not have realized?"

I can't tell her that her problem was being too trusting. Not when I'm here, begging her to open her naïve heart to me one last, undeserved, time.

She digs her manicured nails into the top of the table. Then, as if reminding herself that the nightmare she's experiencing is by no means a dream, she transfers her nails to her skin, simultaneously clasping opposite wrists with the fingers of each hand. Again, she scratches. This time, the surface she's defacing is herself. "I want that bastard arrested."

I reach out across the table. Gently touch her. She realizes what she's doing and stops. Unlike me, she knows hurting herself won't make anything better.

I withdraw my hand. Study my napkin. "Mom, there's a statute of limitations."

She studies hers.

"Besides," I add, "even if there weren't, I just want to let the whole thing go."

Mom's tactical, pragmatic mask dissolves into a puddle of very public tears.

I shouldn't have told her over lunch.

"It's not your fault. I wasn't exactly innocent."

"If only your father hadn't died..."

"I don't think Dad's death had anything to do with it."

Nearby, a couple of the other patrons whisper and point in our direction. Mom notices them noticing her, and, just like that, voila, the mask returns. She dabs away all evidence of emotion and downshifts into information mode.

"I read an article in *The Huffington Post* that claims that daughters whose fathers die or abandon them before the age of ten are five times more likely to seek out unhealthy relationships with men."

"I'm not a statistic. Besides, the past is the past. There's nothing we can do to change it."

She takes an angry forkful of snapper, shoves it into her mouth, and chews.

Anger is better than sadness. I take a bite of my own fish. Savor the flavor.

"What can I do? Can I pay for you to see a therapist? When I think about what he took from you..."

It's the playground again. Her instinct to scoop me up, to rescue me from pain, and to confront the boy who hurt me.

I reach across the table and take my mother's hand. "The only thing Dwight took that I want back is my relationship with you."

She wells up again, but, this time, she spoons out her sadness in measured doses. "I'm glad I never had a child with that man."

I eat some more of my delicious fish and try not to think about the night of the miscarriage.

"Jessica, I am *so* sorry."

"Mom, please, stop apologizing. I'm as guilty as he is. I wanted it."

She waves away my explanation. "You were a child."

We sit in silence for a while.

"That isn't everything. I did a lot of other terrible things to you. Things I'd give anything to undo. I stole money. I lied. I..."

"Oh, Jessica, I know all about that. You don't need to tell me. Whatever you've done, I love you, and I forgive you."

Her tears are tears of sadness. Mine are of gratitude.

≠ 52 ≠

The idea of Scorpion Pose sets off sirens in my cells.

My back writes ransom notes to my mind.

We're holding your vertebra hostage. Give us your alignment, or else.

I ignore its demands. I will not negotiate with terrorists.

Carla and I are at a two-hour Sunday afternoon back-bending workshop at Serenity. Neither of us have been here since rediscovering Rhonda, but we're still on their mailing list. Carla and I were at Starbucks, together, when our phones pinged simultaneously with notifications about today's spinal intensive. Never mind our shared Kama disdain, there was no way either of us was going to miss this.

The 105 minutes preceding these final fifteen have been leading up to this arachnidian moment, wherein the sixteen of us assembled students will attempt this seemingly unattainable backbend.

"You can use the wall," Kama tells us. "If you need to." The way she says it makes it sound like a dare.

But yoga has taught me not to be too proud to honor my limitations, so I drag my mat against a wall, kick up, bend my knees, contort my spine, and perform the impossible.

It's easier than I'd imagined. Well, easier to get in. Now, I have to hold the pose.

As my body remains contorted, my brain seeks an escape. An image surfaces.

I am fifteen, holding Dwight's hand as I lead him toward my bedroom.

I attach words to the recollection.

"Are you sure?" my stepdad asks.

"Of course. Are you?"

"Not at all."

"We love each other," I tell him. "How can it be wrong?"

He lets his lips linger on my forehead—a chaste, parental kiss.

"If it weren't you," I say, "it'd be someone else."

He relents.

I lead.

He follows.

A shockwave of somatic sensation floods my body. I refuse to allow myself to come out of the backbend until every particle of every cell has experienced, and released, its guilt.

"How'd that feel?" Carla asks as soon as I return to my normal, unpretzeled state.

She's opted to stick with Pincha Mayurasana against the Tree of Life so as not to risk a spinal injury. I am anything but injured. Waves of healing relief overwhelm me as remorse over a choice I made eighteen years ago is freed from the prison of my flesh. Scorpion unlocked it, so I could finally let it go.

I bite back tears of gratitude.

"That was awesome," Carla tells me. "You made it look easy."

And, in a way, it was. Easy, and excruciating, and liberating.

"It wasn't easy," I inform her, "but it was worth it."

"I think I might be willing to try. Do you mind spotting me?"

"Not at all."

As happy to get outside myself as I was to break free of the past, I stand at the wall, arms outstretched, ready to keep my friend from falling—willing to rescue her from the uncertainty of attempting something new.

≉ 53 ≉

Sitting across from Chloe in this crowded suburban eatery, I try to read the expression in my sister's impenetrable azure eyes.

Is it pity? Hurt? Contempt? Revulsion?

It's not love. I know love when I see it.

Chloe didn't want to meet me. Mom talked her into it. So, here we are on the first Saturday in April—meeting early because, as my sister informed me on the phone, "I have other things to do with my day."

My failures stack up between us like dominoes. Not that I've ever built anything between us. I've only ever knocked things down.

A year and a half ago, at our cousin Sophie's bachelorette party, when I was thirty-one and Chloe was twenty-seven, she came into a nightclub bathroom a few minutes after I did and found me snorting a line of cocaine off the back of a public toilet seat. If my sister had any remaining vestiges of affection for me, the final drops of her love drained out of her the second she saw me with that straw. That was a few months before the Thanksgiving Day debacle.

I'm surprised, even with Mom's insistence, that Chloe agreed to this.

"Thanks for coming." We've been here long enough to get a table and order and all I've managed to say are the same three obsequious words.

My sister raises one perfectly arched eyebrow and taps her fingers on the tabletop. "Mom said it was important."

"Would you like anything else?" The barista arrives with our lattes. Her exuberance is a welcome diversion from the intensity of Chloe's animosity. "We have some great quiche offerings today! It's nice to see you again, Chloe. I love your highlights."

"Thanks." Chloe smiles at the stranger.

"Just the latte," I say.

"Okay. If you need anything else, just give a holler."

"We will. Renee, this place would fall apart without you." Chloe's tone is syrupy sweet—until our waitress leaves and it's just me and her alone again. "What's this about, Jess?" she demands.

"No Jesse?" Dad used to call us his "e-girls." Chlo-e and Jess-e—two peas in a proverbial pod.

She's not amused. "Seriously, what's up?"

"I wanted to tell you I'm sorry for not being a better sister. I lied to you, stole money from you, violated your trust, and exposed you to situations that you were too young to handle."

"No shit." She takes a sip of her espresso-infused steamed milk.

Behind her rage, I see a little girl with bows in her hair dancing in the kitchen in sock-clad feet while, a room away, I stripped down to my underwear and dry-humped two boxer-clad boys after we'd all smoked a bowl. Sure, I told my sister to stay out of the living room, where my male companions and I were, but Chloe was entitled to coloring books and crayons. Not kitchen exile and a slutty older sister.

I have no shield against the daggers in her eyes. Love renders me defenseless.

"I'm sorry I missed your twenty-first birthday. I'm sorry I ruined Sophie's bachelorette party. I'm sorry for all the times I've hurt you. You deserved better. You *deserve* better. I'd do anything, I'll *do* anything, to make things right between us—if I can."

Something inside her cracks. I see it in the almost imperceptible quiver of her lower lip. She bites down—hard.

"You hurt me, Jess. And a part of me hates you, but another part of me... doesn't."

"Really?"

She nods.

We sip our drinks.

"I know what he did."

"Huh?"

"Dwight."

I can't look at her. Or risk saying or doing the wrong thing. Too much is at stake.

"Did Mom tell you?"

She shakes her head. "I'd hear him going into your room—hear the two of you."

"You did?"

My sister looks past me, into the distance, remembering some long-ago happening. "We were only a wall apart."

"Mom never knew."

"She's always been too trusting."

I take a sip. She does the same.

"I never understood why he chose you."

"What do you mean?"

"For a while, I was actually jealous. You were Daddy's favorite, too."

"Chloe –"

"I know. It's messed up. I understand that now. My therapist and I talked about it."

"You see a therapist?"

"Don't tell Mom. She thinks I've got it all together."

"No one has it all together." As soon as I say it, I realize that it's true.

"I guess I owe you a thank you."

"For what?"

"For keeping me safe. Dr. W said you were a victim so I didn't have to be."

My sister's words rewind my memories until I am face-to-face with Dwight, the tape in my hand issuing the threat that cost me more than I was ready to pay.

If you touch her, I'll have you arrested for molesting me.

I failed to see it then, but I'm struck now by the hurt inscribed in my stepdad's question-mark lips and wide, shocked eyes.

For years, I told myself my attempt at bribery had been an act of bravery. I'd stopped Dwight from going after Chloe, too. I'm not so sure that's true anymore. It was easier to think of Dwight as a pervert than as the great, misguided love of my life. Easier still not to take ownership of the fact that I'd seduced him, or the painful recognition that, even now, even knowing who I am and all I'm capable of, he wants me in a way no man ever has before—a way I fear no man ever will again.

Dwight isn't a pedophile. He's the jagged other half of a puzzle I've spent my whole life trying to solve. But Chloe doesn't need to understand the complexity of what my stepdad and I shared. Telling her would only create more damage.

Made direct amends to such people wherever possible, *except when to do so would injure them or others.*

"That said," she continues, "I'm not ready to forgive you. I need time, and I need you to be a *normal* big sister. I want to be able to come to you for advice on boys, or clothes, or to vent when Mom does something that pisses me off."

"Mom pisses you off?"

"Yes. And you'd know that if you weren't so self-involved."

Ouch. She's right.

"At some point, I'd like to put the past behind us, but only *after* I can trust that you'll be different."

"I understand."

I'd thought my sister would either refuse to let me in at all or open her arms wide—like Mom. I should've known that a parent's capacity for forgiveness is vaster than that of a sibling. Yet, there is something here. Something salvageable.

"I'm still mad at you."

"You should be. I'm mad at me too."

We sit—sipping—in silence for a while. Three tables down from us, a mother wipes drool off her baby's chin.

"I think, deep down, I understand why you did the things you did. You know, Jesse, I wasn't even two when Dad died, so not having him around didn't impact me like it impacted you. That doesn't mean I didn't deserve a better sister, but you deserved better than you got too."

It's my turn to bite my lower lip. "You called me 'Jesse.'"

She nods.

"So..." I force myself to sound breezy. "Are there any boys I can give you advice about? You know, as your new and improved older sister."

Chloe holds up her ring finger and wiggles it.

How could I not have noticed such an enormous diamond? Guess I should add *oblivious* to my list of character defects in need of removal.

"What's his name?" I ask after oohhhing and aahhing for an appropriate amount of time.

"Nathan."

"Are you happy?"

"Absolutely."

"Then, maybe, *you* should be the one giving *me* advice."

She laughs. "Next time. Listen, Jesse, I have to go, but this has been... nice."

"Can I hug you?" I'm surprised by the tentativeness of my tone.

My sister thinks. She takes a sip of her latté. She stands and smooths out the edges of her already smooth shirt. Then, she nods once in the affirmative. I stand too—abruptly—and lunge forward before she can take back her consent.

"I love you, Chloe."

Our embrace is awkward. Forced. Almost as forced as her return "I... you... me too."

Yet, instead of focusing on the effort I know it'll take to rebuild a relationship, I take a breath and am grateful that we've at least made a start.

54

I wake scowling. I've been finished with my eighth step list for what feels like forever, and, even though I've made amends to Mom and Chloe and am starting to rebuild some semblance of a life, I find myself wondering if this is all there is.

Yeah, I'm grateful to be sober, but I'm still a loser. My doctor won't clear me for full-time work until I hit the six-month mark and I'm only at three months and three days.

May 6th. Monday. Outside, it's seventy-four degrees and sunny. Inside, I'm dark and dank and miserable.

I pour myself a bowl of Special K and eat that and a banana, then take a scalding-hot shower where I try, unsuccessfully, to slough off my negativity. Nope. Still there. Guess I'm wearing my I-hate-my-life-so-I'll-wear-all-black-and-look-like-I'm-a-Goth-girl charcoal wife-beater and nondescript matching leggings. I even dig my black Converse out of the back of my closet. I'm in no mood to be colorful.

When I walk into class, my lips twisted into the bitchiest keep-away-from-me face I can muster, I avoid making eye contact with anyone, find a spot in the back corner of the room, set up my mat, and drop into Child's Pose. I'm glad Carla's not here today. As much as I've grown to love her, I don't feel like being around anyone who accepts me. All I want is to slog through the eight a.m. Monday morning Soul Flow class.

I could've waited and gone to the nine a.m. with Rhonda, but I'm avoiding her too. She'd probably intuit my need for an attitude adjustment, and, for this moment anyway, I'm invested in my misery. So, I keep my hips on my heels and my head down and wait for class to begin.

In the safe insularity of Balasana, no one will bother me.

Wrong. Apparently, the perky, boobacious blonde, who works part-time at the front desk, signing people in, and whose name I can never remember, doesn't pick up on my keep-away body language because she sidles up behind me and taps me on the back.

"Jessica!"

I glare at her. She looks like a plastic-surgeried fairy godmother—Glinda the Spandex Good Witch. "Yeah...?"

"Rhonda asked me to make sure you get one of these." She hands me a flier. On it, in eclectic, Zen-style lettering, are the words *Yoga Teacher Training*.

"What's this?" It's a stupid question. I should probably just read the handout.

"We're offering a two-hundred-hour yoga teacher training," Barbie explains. "Each year, every teacher gets to put forth one student who he or she thinks would be a positive addition to our program, the whole staff votes, and then the selected student is offered a scholarship to attend. This year, we've decided to offer it to you."

"Wow. Thanks."

"Yeah. It's like totally free. You just have to buy the books. Think about it, okay? And get back to us a.s.a.p. If you don't want to do it, we'll give the spot to another student, but I know Rhonda was really hoping you'd be part of the program."

I don't have to think. My answer is an emphatic yes.

"I'm in. Thank you, again."

I fold the flier into quadrants and tuck it into the side pocket of my yoga mat bag.

"No biggie. Glad you're on board. And love the outfit."

As Ms. Perky Perfect Tits walks away, it hits me that I'm smiling.

Part IV

Pose

Pigeon Pose (Eka Pada Rajakapotasana)

Come into a tabletop position, on all fours with your knees below your hips. Keep your right knee bent and slide your right shin forward, beneath your torso. Your right ankle will come behind your left wrist. Stretch your left leg behind you on your yoga mat, then fold forward, allowing the weight of your body over your right leg to intensify the stretch in your right hip. After you have fully experienced the hip-opening benefits of this pose on your right side, come back to hands and knees and take this pose on the other side.

Prayer

Eleventh Step Prayer

Lord, make me a channel of thy peace—that where there is hatred, I may bring love—that where there is wrong, I may bring the spirit of forgiveness—that where there is discord, I may bring harmony—that where there is error, I may bring truth—that where there is doubt, I may bring faith—that where there is despair, I may bring hope—that where there are shadows, I may bring light—that where there is sadness, I may bring joy. Lord, grant that I may seek rather to comfort than to be comforted—to understand, than to be understood—to love, than to be loved. For it is by self-forgetting that one finds. It is by forgiving that one is forgiven. It is by dying that one awakens to eternal life.

Promise

"If we are painstaking about this phase of our development, we will be amazed before we are half way through. We are going to know a new freedom and a new happiness. We will not regret the past nor wish to shut the door on it. We will comprehend the word 'serenity' and we will know peace. No matter how far down the scale we have gone, we will see how our experience can benefit others. That feeling of uselessness and self-pity will disappear. We will lose interest in selfish things and gain interest in our fellows. Self-seeking will slip away. Our whole attitude and outlook upon life will change. Fear of people and of economic insecurity will leave us. We will intuitively know how to handle situations which used to baffle us. We will suddenly realize that God is doing for us what we could not do for ourselves. Are these extravagant promises? We think not. They are being fulfilled among us—sometimes quickly, sometimes slowly. They will always materialize if we work for them." (*Alcoholics Anonymous Big Book*, pp. 83-84)

Step Ten:

Continued to take personal inventory, and when we were wrong, promptly admitted it. (Tree Pose)

55

I study my reflection in the full-length dressing-room mirror.

Carla appraises me. "That dress looks amazing on you."

I don't know exactly when it happened, but, at some point, my once concave parts became downright curvaceous.

For a while, my single status and substance-free existence led me into the loving arms of chocolate, but that's died down. Through yoga, I've found a greater awareness of my true hungers and desires. These days, I eat when I'm hungry, stop when I'm full. Sure, I have a tendency to over-caffeinate, but, for the most part, I treat my body well.

I haven't even fucked anyone since Joshua, and that was two months and twenty-five days ago.

"So... You excited for the wedding?"

"More like terrified."

"You're changing, Jess. This is a chance to be different."

Carla's right. I am changing. *Everything* about my life is changing. I'm three months sober, reconciling with my family, and, most exciting of all, I'm about to start yoga teacher training. Yes, I'll miss Jimmy and our burgeoning platonic friendship, but I can't wait to be done dispensing coffee to caffeine junkies. I'm eager to create a life I can be proud of. Not that I'll need, or be able to, quit working at the Free Café anytime soon. But there's an end in sight. And, come to think of it, a beginning.

"Aren't you gonna buy anything?"

Carla examines her own reflection. "Not until I lose my seven I'm-in-mourning-because-my-husband-is-gay pounds. How'd you let me get so fat?"

I fiddle with the zipper on my dress and keep my mouth shut. There's no winning this argument.

"Seriously, Jess. That's the dress."

"You think so?"

"If you don't buy it, I'll hate you forever."

"Well, we can't have that..."

After I pay for my purchases and we make a quick stop at the smoothie place for a couple of their classic concoctions—Mango-A-Go-Go for her, and Pomegranate Paradise for me—Carla and I leave the King of Prussia Mall and head to Branches.

“Thanks again for coming with me. The last time I went to a family event, I mangled the whole thing.”

“Sure. What’re friends for? Besides, this thing is delicious.” She holds up her bright orange masterpiece.

I smile and accelerate. I don’t want to be late. Carla and I have started going to Rhonda’s Friday Night Advanced Vinyasa Flow class. At first, I was afraid to do something I used to do when I was using, but Rhonda’s vinyasa classes aren’t like my old Sati classes. Or, maybe, they are and I’m not the same me I used to be.

Every time my favorite teacher leads us through an intense physical practice, I revel in each attempt that leads nowhere, each failed try. When I skip a vinyasa and take rest in Child’s Pose, there’s no recrimination. Only redemption. It feels good to give myself permission not to be perfect. To let every unsuccessful effort act as an invitation to accept myself exactly where I am.

Sometimes, as Rhonda leads the class through a series of reverent Sun Salutations, I even find myself silently praying to a God I’m just beginning to believe in.

56

When Chloe called, sixteen days before her wedding, to ask if I'd like to attend, I said, "Absolutely."

So what if everyone else received their invitations months ago? I don't blame my sister for being unsure about me. The truth is, sometimes, I'm still not sure about myself.

I'm not invited to the reception—only to the ceremony—and, while it's painful not to be fully incorporated into my sister's special day, we're making a start and that'll have to be enough.

"I'm glad you're here," Mom whispers for what feels like the hundredth time this hour. "It makes me happy to see you girls working through your issues."

"Me too."

"And your dress is lovely. Very appropriate."

I try not to cringe as I think about years' worth of miniskirts and fuck-me pumps.

The bridal march begins to play, and we all stand—like one en masse wave at a baseball game.

There must be at least two hundred people here—all of whom will be heading from the church to the banquet hall. At first, I felt left out, but, after a conversation with April, I got honest with myself and admitted that the idea of a wedding reception—all that alcohol and all those drunken, single strangers—was overwhelming at this stage of my sobriety.

Chloe is a vision in taffeta and lace and her soon-to-be-father-in-law is beaming as he walks her down the aisle. Last week, the two of us went over to Mom's to help her box up Dwight's unclaimed belongings and my little sister told me that her fiancé's dad has become like a surrogate father to her.

"It's sweet that Nathan's dad is giving Chloe away," I say, so low that only Mom can hear.

As she snots into her handkerchief, my mother's reply is barely audible. "I wish your father could see this."

"Maybe, he can."

As I watch her walk toward her new life as a married, grown-up, responsible *wife*, I don't worry about whether my sister is making the right choice, or whether she'll be happy in the long run. Chloe is an adult, fully capable of making her own decisions. More capable, by far, than I am.

"Dearly beloved, we are gathered here today, in the presence of God and each other, to join Chloe Leonard and Nathan Tarrington in holy matrimony."

My sister's fiancé is a tall, handsome man with an aquiline nose and eyes that brighten whenever he sees her. Mom told me earlier today that the way Nathan looks at Chloe is the way Daddy looked at her.

And, I thought, the way Dwight once looked at me.

After the vows and "I dos" and requisite kissing of the bride, Mom and I and the rest of the guests filter outside for the culminating, ceremonial act before they head to the reception and I go back to my apartment to change out of my dress and into my pajamas.

A trainer carries a cage into the center of the churchyard. We all go silent as we wait, expectantly, for what's about to happen.

"This is an old custom," my new brother-in-law tells the massive throng of smiling guests.

"But that's because we're old souls." Chloe's tone is wedding bells and bridal bouquets.

"To innocence and love," Nathan says.

"And new beginnings," his wife adds.

I don't look up at the doves as they're released—beautiful and white-winged—into the sky. Instead, I focus on the pitiful, unnoticed creature who lies, writhing, on the hard, packed earth. I stoop down, pick up the bird, and see the reason for her struggle: a severed wing. A red gash derived from some unknown injury prevents her from joining her flapping, flying flock.

Holding the tiny dove, I can't help but think of Flying Pigeon Pose, a posture that is hard for me to hold because my arms never quite feel strong enough to support me. Yet, as I cradle the broken bird, I recognize that its magnificence is not to be found in the air, but on the ground, in the struggle.

"I'll call you 'King,'" I tell her.

It's an odd choice of name seeing as how I've decided that the bird is female—and because she's a dove, not a pigeon. But so what? I've never named a pet before. Chloe named our childhood dog "Santa Cruz" after her two favorite men—Santa Claus and Tom Cruise, whose movies Daddy said we were too young to watch, although he let us see the scenes where Cruz threw bottles in the air in *Cocktail* and danced around the living room in *Risky Business*. Chloe had only ever heard Cruise's name said aloud.

"King," I repeat, liking the sound of it.

When the handler approaches, she's apologetic. "I'm sorry. This one tried to escape her cage" (So it *is* a her!) "and hurt herself. I don't know why my assistant brought her. She's in no way ready to fly."

She holds out her hand.

I shake my head. I'm not giving the dove back. Not now. Not ever.

"Can I buy her?"

The bird lady studies me. "I dunno what you want with a useless dove. She might never fully recover."

"I don't care if she can fly. I like her as she is."

Ten bucks and ten minutes later, King and I are in my Hyundai—me at the wheel, she my injured passenger. Instead of going straight to my apartment, I drive to PetSmart where I buy her gourmet birdseed, a tree-shaped perch, and a cage to call her own.

57

Yoga teacher training is already harder than expected, and we haven't even started. Not officially anyway. Before our first session, we had to read three books (*Yoga Anatomy* by Leslie Kaminoff, *Light on Yoga* by B.K.S. Iyengar, and *The Mirror of Yoga: Awakening the Intelligence of Body and Mind* by Richard Freeman) and write a reflection paper on each. It feels a lot like high school, except that I actually care about what I'm learning and I'm not cutting any classes.

I expected endless Namastes and Shavasana shoulder rubs, but this is rapid-fire instructions, tears, and personal revelations. Ten twenty-hour weekends in a row. What was I thinking?

On our first day of training, which is also the first day of June, and National Dare Day, Cadence, Branches' owner, lets us in and I suddenly turn into a geeked-out-groupie.

"Calm down, Jess," Carla whispers.

Evidently, I'm smiling so wide it appears as if my face might shatter.

Carla is doing the training with me. She doesn't want to teach, but she says she needs something to keep herself from focusing on how much she misses Tim. Evidently, like mine, her longing ebbs and flows.

It's impossible not to be awestruck. Our second instructor—Kaur Bhajan—is a legend. I can't believe he's agreed to come to Philadelphia for ten weekends in a row to teach a bunch of nobodies how to instruct others in the art and discipline of yoga. The first thing Kaur Bhajan tells us is that his mission is to help us swim through our sorrows and find salvation.

As far as I'm concerned, AA is already doing that, but I jot down *swim through sorrow* in my new Celtic mandala journal, purchased for the sole purpose of taking teacher training notes, and keep my mouth shut. Or, well, silent and gaping.

I was bummed when I found out Rhonda isn't going to be involved in our training. Carla and I asked Cadence about it, but all she said was "Rhonda's having a few personal problems. Nothing serious. She just can't take on any more commitments right now."

"Do you think that's part of why she stopped teaching at Kama's studio?" Carla asks after the studio owner walks away.

I shrug. "Kama is a first-rate bitch. I don't know how anyone could work for her."

Cadence clanks her beautiful brass tingsha together—our cue that it is time to begin.

The gentle sounds reverberate throughout the room in a cacophony of serenity. They should use tingsha in AA. Maybe, I'll suggest them at the next business meeting.

We take our seats, cross-legged on our mats. Nine eager pupils—Carla, Jake, Marcy, Susan, Brenda, Tricia, Larry, Lucy and, of course, me.

"The best way to begin is to be vulnerable," Kaur Bhajan tells us. "To expose our pain to the light and embrace whatever shadows are illuminated."

Cadence explains his esoteric utterance in simpler terms. "We'd like each of you to share one thing that makes you feel exposed—something personal, true, and, maybe, a little painful. Carla, let's start with you."

My friend shares that her husband of four years left her because he's gay. Then, we go around the room in a clockwise circle, each telling a secret to a room full of strangers. Jake talks about being bullied as a child, Marcy reveals that she has an eating disorder, Susan tells us that her father was physically abusive and used to regularly beat her and her siblings while her mother did nothing to stop it, Brenda divulges that she was molested as a child, Tricia speaks about being in a loveless marriage but not feeling strong enough to leave it, Larry opens up about having an affair and feeling ashamed, and Lucy's eyes water as she tells us about her heartbreak at discovering (last year, after the woman who raised her since birth died of ovarian cancer) that she'd been adopted as an infant.

I'm the last to share.

"Wow," I say. "I have so many shadows. I'm a recovering addict and alcoholic and, back when I was a teenager, I had a sexual relationship with my ex-stepdad."

We are broken people—bonded together, not in spite of our flaws, but because of them.

"Each of us has a past," Cadence tells us. "Yoga is a way of excavating our truest, deepest, most precious, parts. We come to our mats to meet ourselves, to remember our pasts, to envision our futures and, most importantly, to pull ourselves back to the present. Because it is in the present that true transformation happens."

Kaur Bhajan piggybacks on her sentiments. "And the surest way to connect with ourselves in the present moment is by breathing."

We spend the next several hours talking about inhaling and exhaling—ujjayi, kapalabhati, nadhi sodahana, and sithali-style.

"How do we give verbal cues to our future students, to teach them how to breathe," the adopted girl—Lucy—asks, and Kaur Bhajan launches into a fifteen-minute tutorial.

I take three more pages of notes while Carla sketches a complicated diagram that looks like a diaphragm with a bunch of directional arrows pointing to and away from it.

"Never forget that breath is life," Kaur Bhajan instructs. "That is why it is so essential."

"Isn't it ironic?" Brenda observes. "We come into this world knowing how to take life in, but, somewhere along the line, we unlearn how to inhale."

I jot down *Breath is life. Learn how to take it in* in my notebook.

Kaur Bhajan nods. "That's an incredibly astute observation. Let's go even deeper. Yoga is a spiritual discipline. We use it to go inward, so that we can go upward. The physical practice is mere preparation for enlightenment. The asanas, the poses, ready our bodies and prepare our minds for Corpse Pose, which is, essentially, where we connect with the Divine."

Larry laughs. "So, over the next month, you'll teach us how to connect to God and prepare for death?"

The other eight of us chuckle along, grateful for the infusion of humor. But our instructors, like so many spiritually-evolved souls, sail straight over Larry's sarcasm and completely miss the joke.

"God is in you already," Cadence replies.

Kaur Bhajan nods. "You must practice letting go of the internal and external clutter so, when you go inside, your vision is no longer obscured, and you can see and feel the Divine."

"Shit," I say, "that's deep."

Then, I inhale.

Step Eleven:

Sought through prayer and meditation to improve our conscious contact with God *as we understood Him*, praying only for knowledge of His will for us and the power to carry that out. (Triangle Pose)

≠ 58 ≠

As I close my eyes to begin this morning's meditation, I think, *I'm glad I peed*, then, *Did I turn the light off in the bathroom?*

I get up, assure myself that I did, indeed, turn off the lights, return to my meditation cushion, reset the timer, and start over.

I'm the worst at meditation. Intentional mental emptying is completely different from drunken blacking out. I like clearing my mind, but, more often than not, I'll wander away from thinking about my breath and end up on a five-minute mental detour before bringing myself back. The trick is to allow the thought, thank it, then return to my desired point of focus. Sometimes, it works. Others, it doesn't.

April says it's not about being good or bad. It's about having a daily, personal, spiritual discipline. "Sitting for twenty minutes every day is a small investment compared to the 24/7 work of maintaining an active addiction."

I'm not just meditating for eleventh-step reasons. It's also one of the requirements of teacher training.

For a program that's offering a path to relaxation and Zen, squeezing twenty hours of instruction in ten back-to-back weekends interspersed with throughout-the-week required readings, daily movement and meditation practices, seems counterintuitive. Yet, I'm glad Branches' program is an accelerated one. The weekend it ends, I'll have exactly six months sober, but, when I'm cleared to get off disability, instead of going back to working full-time at the Free Café, my plan is to stick with a part-time coffee-serving schedule and augment that income with teaching yoga.

I bring my attention back to my meditation cushion—a gift from Carla after she found out I'd opted to sit on my yoga mat rather than part with fifty bucks for a proper relaxation setup. I have to admit, a cushion is more comfortable.

Cadence is encouraging each of us to find a technique that works for us, so I've been experimenting with Visualization, Mandalas, Healing, Light, Astral, Sound, Breathing, Mantra, Transcendental, and Guided meditations. I've even gone with April to her Buddhist meditation center. Not that I'm about to become a Buddhist. Or a Catholic—despite the fact that, since my sister got back from her honeymoon, I've joined Mom and Chloe at church a few times.

I find God in yoga studios and twelve step rooms.

I focus on my breath. Then, on the rumbling in my belly. Then, on what I want for breakfast. Then, on how I'm almost out of coffee. Then, on the plight of starving children in Africa. Then, on how cool it would be to take a safari. Then, on how well King's coming along.

Oh crap. I pull my attention back to my breath.

Inhale. Exhale.

I'm glad King's doing better. Her injured wing is almost completely mended. One day, I feel certain, she'll fly.

Exhale. Inhale.

It isn't until close to the end of my allotted twenty minutes that a wave of contentment washes over me and, just as in almost every practice, I experience a fleeting moment of feeling at home inside my skin. Then, just that quickly, my mind jumps in with an analysis.

I'm four and a half months sober—and four months celibate. Of course, I'm experiencing shifts. My whole life is different. I like it. Except the no sex part. One day at a time without alcohol is one thing, but, since that first time at fifteen, this is the longest I've ever gone without the familiar friction of a man. My thoughts meander further down the celibacy road—obsessing about what it'll be like when I do have sex again. Hopefully, it'll be with someone I care about, possibly even love. Someone of an apostolic nature, perhaps.

How can I be thinking about this during *meditation*?

I shouldn't be imagining Paul's Birkenstocks beside my bed, his arms and legs intertwined with mine. I should be developing my unfolding relationship with my Higher Power, which should be the most important relationship in my life.

The timer goes off and rescues me from any more unwanted introspection.

Coffee, I think.

And that's the end of that.

≠ 59 ≠

"Oh hi, Jessica!"

"Hi."

Damn. I forget her name. It starts with a D.

"It's Dottie, dear." She's sweet to let me off the hook for my inability to commit her appellation to memory.

"Oh yeah. Dottie. How are you? Funny running into you here."

It's the Fourth of July—not exactly a day I'd expect to run into someone I know at the grocery store, but I'm out of hummus, rice cakes and bottled water and need to stock up for this weekend's teacher training.

Later tonight, Carla, April and I are taking Erika and Annabelle to see the fireworks at Penn's Landing. Howie is traveling for work so, as Erika said when she invited me, "It'll be just us girls."

I'd already made plans with Carla and was initially skeptical about combining worlds, but I'm learning to be more integrated—and more authentic—so, when April and her girls told me Carla was invited too, I called my closest friend and asked if, instead of just the two of us sitting on her couch watching *Independence Day*, we could broaden the scope of our holiday plans.

Dottie peers into my basket. "My, you do eat healthy."

Dottie is one of the OA/AA crossover contingent. She's been sober from drugs and alcohol for forever, but her overeating is clearly still an issue. Her cart is full of diet foods and binge foods in equal quantities.

"I try," I tell her.

She chomps on an obnoxiously large wad of gum.

"Yeah, I know. I should be filling my God-hole, but, instead, I fill my pie-hole."

Ironically, Dottie has a pie in her cart. Apple, the best kind.

I nod. "Do you have any more of that gum?"

She laughs. "It's silly, really. I'm an old woman, but I can't resist a gumball machine."

"Huh?"

She gestures toward the front of the store where assorted golf-ball-sized gumballs glitter from behind their glass enclosure.

"I haven't had a gumball since I was little."

Dottie rummages around in her purse and hands me a quarter. "My treat."

"Thanks."

"You know, watching you get sober has been a real inspiration."

"It has?"

"Sure. Newcomers help me not to forget what it was like."

"Speaking of forgetting... Seeing that can of tuna in your cart just reminded me—I need to buy a can opener."

She chuckles. "Girl, you don't have a can opener?"

I smirk. "Nope. And I almost forgot to buy one."

"Next time," she advises, "put it on your list."

"Never underestimate the power of a list," I agree. "Shopping or otherwise."

Dottie gets the reference.

* * *

It's so crowded the only place to sit is on the ground, so I'm on a threadbare blanket on the Penn's Landing promenade. Annabelle is on my lap because she says I'm more comfortable than concrete.

Not exactly a ringing endorsement, but I'll take what I can get.

April smiles as the sky explodes. "You look happy, Jess."

I snuggle against her daughter—love on loan, to be returned at the end of the night. "I am."

"I'm happy too!" Annabelle points at the sky. A cacophony of color—red and blue and yellow and green, the light and the rainbow simultaneously.

Erika and Carla are off buying Funnel Cake from one of the food trucks. Despite her self-directed judgments, Carla hasn't committed to taking the actions that will lead to her losing those pesky post-break-up pounds.

I get it. Sometimes, it takes a while to become ready to stop avoiding the void and start taking the necessary actions to achieve a goal. I wish she wouldn't be so hard on herself though. When she's ready, she'll do what it takes.

"Jess, how come you don't have kids?"

"Annabelle!" April scolds.

"It's okay," I say and hold her daughter closer. "That's a good question, kiddo," I tell my innocent inquirer. "I guess I don't have them because I used to not be very good at taking care of myself, so I wouldn't have made a good mom to someone else."

"And now you're good at it?"

"Better."

"Mommy used to be bad too, before she had us. She's a alkalolic."

I laugh. April joins in. Annabelle crawls half into her mother's lap while remaining half in mine.

"You know," I whisper, "I'm an alkalolic too."

"Well, I'm glad you're better now. I like you this way."

I like me this way too. The thought arises like a lotus out of muck, unexpected and magnificent, and I hold onto it the same way I'm holding the child in my arms—grateful for all it offers, aware that it didn't come from me, and fully cognizant that this moment is fleeting and, like everything else, it too will pass.

≠ 60 ≠

My phone rings. *Mom.* I programmed her in a few months ago—when I realized that, no matter what the future holds, I want her in my life.

"It's done." I'm not completely sure what my mother is talking about, but the exuberance in her voice is contagious.

"What is?"

"I called Dwight and told him that, if he didn't sign immediately, I'd out him as a child molester and take him for all he's worth. So, he agreed to give me everything I asked for and signed the papers this afternoon."

"Papers?" I was in the middle of studying Sanskrit and am finding it difficult to compute this new, unexpected information.

"Divorce. There's a ninety-day mandatory waiting period in the state of Pennsylvania, so it's not all *finalized*, but the important thing is there's money for you. A lot of money."

"Mom –"

"I know it'll never be enough, but –"

"I don't want money." The addict in me immediately disagrees. *Yes, you do. You earned it.* I take a deep breath and respond the way I know I need to if I have any hope of remaining in recovery. "I'm not ready to have 'a lot of money' yet. I haven't been sober long enough."

July 7th, 2019—the one year anniversary of my leap off a stranger's roof. I've been sober five months and four days.

"That's silly, Jessica. You could stop working at that coffee shop and do what makes you happy: travel, explore, get... help."

I think about April and the people I'm coming to know, through their shares at meetings. And Carla. "I have help. And, right now, the only place I want to be is here."

"Well, how about I put it aside for you? For when you're ready..."

"Can I talk to my sponsor and get back to you?"

"Of course, sweetheart."

"Hey, Mom...?"

"Yes, Jessica."

"Thank you for not blaming me. And thanks for the offer. I don't know if I'll take you up on it. It feels dirty to accept money from him, but I appreciate you wanting to help."

"Don't be silly. If I can do *anything* to make up for –"

"Mom, it's not your mistake. It was mine. And his."

"His, Jessica. *His.*" Before I can reply, she adds, "Dwight's an ass. I'm only sorry I didn't see it sooner."

As soon as we get off the phone, I pull out my well-worn copy of the *Big Book*, turn to page 83 and read the ninth step promises:

> If we are painstaking about this phase of our development, we will be amazed before we are halfway through. We are going to know a new freedom and a new happiness. We will not regret the past nor wish to shut the door on it. We will comprehend the word "serenity" and we will know peace. No matter how far down the scale we have gone, we will see how our experience can benefit others. That feeling of uselessness and self-pity will disappear. We will lose interest in selfish things and gain interest in our fellows. Self-seeking will slip away. Our whole attitude and outlook upon life will change. Fear of people and of economic insecurity will leave us. We will intuitively know how to handle situations which used to baffle us. We will suddenly realize that God is doing for us what we could not do for ourselves. Are these extravagant promises? We think not. They are being fulfilled among us-sometimes quickly, sometimes slowly. They will always materialize if we work for them.

I don't feel as if I've fully achieved the results of having done my ninth step yet. True, good things are beginning to happen. I'm getting better. Life is getting better. Shame is sloughing off me, as, with each new, honorable act, I exfoliate the outer epidermis of my acting out behavior. Yet, my initial, gut-level response isn't always what I'd hope for. I'm still baffled by a lot of situations, and I don't always believe in God enough to realize that He's doing for me what I can't.

I pick up the phone. "Hi, April."

"Hey Jess."

"I want to ask for your opinion about something."

"What's up?"

"My mom wants to give me money. And, the thing is, as much as I want to take it, I'm worried that having access to too much cash might be counterproductive at this point. Besides, she's getting it from Dwight as part of their divorce settlement, so it'd be kind of like payment for services rendered."

"I tell you what... Why don't you have her put it in an account that you can't touch until you have five years sober?"

"*Five* years?"

"Sure. The first year you're still a mess and any major changes are likely to take you out, and, I'm not gonna lie, year two tends to be hard too because you're still struggling to define yourself and break free from your old identity. After that, you start getting to know yourself and building a life that reflects who you are. That's hard to do if you don't have to work for things and struggle and make mistakes. Money will rob you of the chance to find yourself—by yourself."

"Five years, huh?"

"Five. If you decide, after that, not to take the money, you can always give it to a charity or something. You need time to find what's right for you. Having too much too soon can be a setup for failure."

"Five years..."

"It's just a suggestion."

It's a good one. Before I lose my nerve, I hang up, hit the redial button, and tell my mother what April and I have worked out. Against all my inner instincts, I even instruct her to have the lawyers draw up the paperwork to say that I can collect the money not five years from today, but after having attained five years of continuous sobriety. That way, if I slip, I have to start over.

"Alright, Jessica," Mom agrees. "I'm proud of you."

"I'm proud of me, too," I tell her.

For choosing to prioritize recovery over the easy out, and for believing that I will, eventually, get five years of continuous sobriety.

Step Twelve:

Having had a spiritual awakening as the result of these steps, we tried to carry this message to other addicts, and to practice these principles in all our affairs. (Corpse Pose)

≠ 61 ≠

April has been encouraging me to start sponsoring.

"But I'm not ready," I protest. "I have no clue how to help someone else."

She blows on her hibiscus and honey tea and arches an eyebrow.

"Besides, what if I get a sponsee who's a hot mess?"

"You mean like you used to be?"

"Exactly."

Through the open window, I can hear Howie and the girls playing a contented game of tag in their perfectly-manicured backyard.

"Not it!" someone screams.

"Got you!"

A gleeful chuckle. A bird chirps to a friend. King's wing is fully healed. Any day now, I plan to take her to a nearby wildlife preserve and let her fly. Away.

"Seriously, April, I can't get someone like that sober."

My sponsor takes a sip of her now appropriately-temperatured tea. "You can't get anyone sober. Only a Higher Power can do that."

"I know, but..."

"Anything after *but* is bullshit."

"Tell me how you really feel." I slurp my coffee and smile. I know I'm getting better, but I don't have what it takes to sponsor. I'm not wise or intuitive or patient or loving.

"If God wants me to sponsor," I declare, "He'll give me a sponsee."

"Do me a favor..."

I cringe in advance. "Okay...?"

"Pray about it."

"That's it?"

April drains the last vestiges from her cup. "That's it."

"Sure." Praying I can do.

Still, I'm only humoring her. After I go back to my apartment, leaving April with her husband and kids and I-have-it-all-together life, I offer up a halfhearted, half-assed "God, if I'm ready, bring me a sponsee."

I have more important things to think about than helping some train-wreck addict.

I have only two more weekends before I finish yoga teacher training. My new life is about to begin.

On Friday morning, I arrive at class half an hour early because I'm hoping Rhonda will be sitting beneath the Tree of Life, and I'll be able to ask her to show me a few adjustment techniques.

Good, I think when I notice that my teacher's VW is the only car in the parking lot, but then I see that the lights are off.

I jiggle the door handle.

Locked.

I knock.

Nothing.

I knock again.

Still nothing.

It takes several poundings with my fist before Rhonda comes to the door.

"I'm sorry." She wipes at her red eyes. "I didn't hear you."

"What's wrong?"

My teacher's naked look of pain is a mirror—reflecting back the version of the me I used to be. "I have a problem."

I wrap my arms around her. "What're you using?" I whisper into her thick mass of hair.

Rhonda pulls back. Her mask slips off, then returns, then slips off again. She tries—unsuccessfully—to put it back on, but the self, once revealed, cannot be concealed.

"I'm fine, really. I don't know why I said anything. I just had a shitty night last night."

"What're you using?" I repeat.

She stares at the ground.

I rummage through my purse, dig out my twenty-four-hour sober coin, and hand it to her.

When my teacher looks up at me, there is hope intermingled with remorse. She shakes her head. "I'm not supposed to be this person."

"You mean human?"

For an instant, Rhonda's bloodshot eyes brighten, revealing the version of herself that shines through in her teaching.

"I needed a lot of help to get sober," I tell her. "And, if you'll let me, I'd like to help you."

Rhonda nods. "It didn't used to be this bad, but, lately, I've been spiraling out of control."

"What is it? Heroin? Coke? Meth?"

She takes my hand and traces a capital *H* in my palm with her index finger, as if she is unable to say the word out loud.

"If I find you help, will you'll take it? No questions asked?"

"Sure, Jess. I trust you."

She trusts *me.* The words pierce through my insecurities and perceived inadequacies.

I tell Rhonda I'm skipping yoga today. I have something more important to do. "Just teach your class," I say. "Let me worry about the rest."

As people start arriving, my teacher plasters on a smile and assumes an aura of enlightenment. I wait for the last of the students to trickle in before taking out my phone and making the necessary calls. I try three different treatment centers before I find somewhere with an available bed that accepts insurance and can do a same-day intake.

"I'll have her there this afternoon," I promise.

Then, I place the fourth call.

"Hello."

"Hi, Cadence. It's Jess, from teacher training."

"Oh sure, Jess. How are you?"

"I'm okay. I'm here at the studio. Everything's fine. Rhonda's teaching her class right now. But, the thing is, she has a medical issue and needs treatment for it. I think it'll be a few weeks, maybe even a month, before she'll be able to come back to teaching."

"I knew something was up. She hasn't been herself lately. Is she alright? What's the issue?"

"She'll be fine. She'd have called you herself, but, like I said, she has to teach."

I leapfrog over the specifics and offer up some vague explanation about me agreeing to deal with logistics so my favorite teacher can make an announcement at the end of class letting people know what to expect. Rhonda's recovery is hers to disclose—or not—as she decides.

"Do you think you can get coverage for her classes?"

"Actually…" Cadence's tone is infused with her smile. "The timing is pretty perfect. I can work it out so our teacher training graduates take over her classes."

"You'll give them back to her though, right? When she's ready…?"

"Of course. Rhonda's indispensable."

I jot down a few details on a bright yellow Post-it note.

Treatment, three to four weeks.

Cadence will get coverage for classes.

All okay.

You'll come back better than ever.

Then, I open the door a crack. Rhonda sees my outstretched hand in the low, flickering candlelight, takes the note from me, then eases the door shut again. I sit at the desk and breathe in the feeling of usefulness while trying not to obsess about how much I'll miss Rhonda's classes while she's away, getting help.

A little while later, students begin filtering out.

"She's such a gifted teacher," one of them remarks as the door slams shut behind her. "I wish she weren't taking time off."

"Oh, I *know*," another says. "Yoga is my *religion*."

Rhonda is the last to emerge. Her smile is tissue-paper thin. "So, now you know. I'm a fraud."

"You're human," I assure her. "You're gonna get help, and you'll be back here, teaching, in a month."

"Promise?"

"Promise. *If* you do the work, follow the program, and get a sponsor."

62

The phone startles me awake. Shit. I forgot to turn my ringer off. I stumble out of bed and across the room, rummage around in my purse, and find the culprit of my annoyance. The last thing I need is for my sleep to be interrupted. I spent the earlier part of today driving my yoga teacher turned sponsee to a treatment facility. Then I cleaned my apartment, made myself a tuna fish sandwich, went to a meeting, did a few hours of teacher training homework, and lay in bed until nearly two a.m. ruminating about how scared I am that I'm going to fuck up this new, awesome life that I'm building for myself.

The phone rings again.

"Hello." My voice is groggy and thick with sleep.

The number on my caller ID reads *Blocked.*

"Carla...?"

My friend's speech is so high-pitched and panicked that I can't make out anything she's trying to tell me.

"Carla. Slow down. What's wrong?"

I hear her sharp intake of breath. She begins again. "It's Tim. He got in a fight with his boyfriend. I'm at the hospital. He's going to be here overnight. The doctors say I can bring him home tomorrow."

Today tomorrow or tomorrow tomorrow? It's 4:17 a.m.

"What hospital?"

"Bryn Mawr." The same one where Daddy died.

Carla's still talking. "It's really bad, Jess. Tim's a mess. Broken bones and a black eye. I feel so guilty. I was so mad that he hurt me that I wanted something bad to happen to him."

"Carla, it's okay. You didn't cause this."

As soon as I say the words, I feel a wave of nausea and see my father's face.

You didn't cause this. Except that I did.

But I can't wallow. Carla needs me.

"Take a deep breath," I say. She does. I do, too. "I'll be right there."

Thirty minutes later, I arrive at Bryn Mawr Hospital with two large coffees and a bag full of muffins. We have to be at the studio at nine, and, if we're going to make it through ten hours of practice and instruction, caffeine is a necessity.

Carla hugs me and takes a muffin out of the bag. "Thanks for coming!"

"Of course. So, what, exactly, happened?"

"Tim's always been too trusting." I listen as my friend launches into an explanation about how her soon-to-be ex-husband's new boyfriend is abusive. "This isn't the first time he's hurt Tim," she tells me. "But it is the worst."

"Did you know about this?"

"Of course not. Tim didn't want to admit it. He's too proud."

We sip our coffees. Eat our muffins.

"I feel terrible. I actually told him, when he left, that I hoped his new guy hurt him as much as he'd hurt me."

I reach out. Take her hand. Squeeze. "You didn't mean it. And, even if you did, you're not responsible." It's as if, in offering Carla redemption, I'm shining the light of forgiveness on my five-year-old self. Even after step work, exposure, confession, six Hail Marys, and the passage of twenty-eight years, I haven't felt completely absolved. I still don't. Not completely, but I do feel a small shift.

April is right. It's in giving to others that I'm finally able to receive.

"Is it wrong that a part of me is glad this happened, happy he'll be coming home?"

"Not at all."

I don't have the heart to tell my friend that her unwavering fidelity to and love for her gay husband is codependent. Carla doesn't need advice. She needs understanding. So, I listen. I've learned how to listen—first on the mat, then in meetings.

≠ 63 ≠

What is this, an AA field trip?

Looking around the room, I see a sea of familiar faces. April and Dottie and Charlene and Trey and Oliver and others—so many others. Even Paul is here, his body stooped in Child's Pose, waiting and reverent. There must be at least fifteen people from the AA rooms—at *my* yoga studio.

I glance down at my color-changing ring—the one Trey gave me on our Captain Ahab's date. I've held onto the remembrance, if not to the relationship.

I guess you'd say
What can make me feel this way?

The ring shifts from pink to yellow. I squeeze it, like a talisman, and watch it morph to a purplish blue.

I pause. Take a deep breath. Tell myself to let fear wash through me like a wave, and to resist the temptation to go for a ride—or to be swept under.

These people aren't invading my space. They're supporting me in my spiritual evolution.

As I think back over the past year and a half—the meetings, the prayers, the hours on my mat, the shitty meditation sessions, the moments of transcendence, the steps—and their accompanying promises—I'm rendered breathless by the magnitude of just how much has changed. And, then, Paul looks up from his on-the-mat huddle and smiles at me with that familiar rakish grin and I can exhale.

The pieces of my life are finally starting to fit together. After class, I'm going to tell him I'm ready for that cup of coffee—assuming, that is, that his offer still stands. But, for now, I have something more important to do.

"Come to stand at the top of your mat," I instruct.

One by one, they turn their faces to me, waiting to be led through the same series of poses that has brought me closer to knowing and loving myself, that has eclipsed the highs of drinking and drugging.

They are ready.

Am I?

There's only one way to find out.

"Let's begin," I say.

Acknowledgements

In 2007, when I was killing myself with bulimia, my best friend, Sarah, told me I was the food equivalent of a junkie.

"You're an addict," she said. "You need help."

Shortly thereafter, my boyfriend, Roger, took me with him to an AA meeting because even though I'm not now, nor have I ever been, an alcoholic, he knew I needed a spiritual solution to stop my cycle of self-destruction. I've long since ceased attending AA meetings, but I am in recovery today.

As I progressed from pain to purpose, I discovered a number of spiritual and self-help practices, one of which was yoga. Regularly engaging in the art and discipline of yoga stilled my racing thoughts and helped heal deep emotional wounds. It has become an integral part of my life. In fact, I'm now a certified yoga teacher.

Although this book is a work of fiction, I was inspired to write it as a direct result of my own journey to recovery. Throughout the writing and editing process, I found myself reflecting on how I never would have been able to recover without the support and encouragement of friends, family members and professionals. Thank you to each and every one of you. You know who you are.

About the Author

When Daralyse Lyons isn't doing splits or jumping out of airplanes, this former yoga teacher and eternal adrenaline junkie can be found with pen in hand furiously scribbling her latest novel. To date, she has written more than two dozen full-length books, a handful of short stories and countless articles. A member of the National Association of Black Journalists (NABJ), the host of a successful podcast, an actress, a storyteller, and a summa cum laude graduate of NYU, Daralyse brings intelligence and enthusiasm to all her endeavors.

Learn more at **www.DaralyseLyons.com**

Study Guide

Part I:

1. What are your initial impressions of Jessica?
2. What purpose do the yoga postures in this book serve?
3. How important are mentors, in life and in recovery?
4. What purpose does denial serve in maintaining an addiction?
5. How do you understand Jessica's relationship with her stepdad?
6. What is the importance of sisterhood in a story that takes place in the City of Brotherly Love?
7. Guess the identity of the man Jessica sees in the crowd.

Part II:

8. What is the relationship between honesty and wisdom?
9. Has Jessica hit her bottom?
10. How important is humility to recovery?
11. Why doesn't April give up on Jessica?
12. How do the relationships with Daddy and Dwight impact the ways in which Jessica relates to men?
13. What do you think of Carla?
14. Does the introduction of Paul complicate the narrative? If so, how?
15. What could Jessica have done to avoid a relapse?
16. What role do you think Rhonda will play in Jessica's life?

Part III:

17. How much do perceptions acquired during childhood influence us as adults?
18. What do you anticipate will happen between Jessica and Paul?
19. What do you think of Jessica's realization that drugs and alcohol were her solution, as opposed to her problem?
20. What are your reactions to Garrett?

21. Do you agree with Jessica's assessment that she and Charlene are "exactly the same"? Why or why not?
22. What is the role of confession in this novel?
23. What is the purpose of prayer?
24. Discuss the complexity of Jessica's relationship with her mother.

Part IV:

25. Have your opinions about Jessica shifted over the course of the book? If so, how?
26. How important do you think spirituality is to recovery?
27. What do you think of Chloe waiting so long to invite Jessica to her wedding? If you were in Chloe's shoes, would you have done the same?
28. Discuss the concept of imperfect meditation.
29. Why doesn't Jessica feel ready to be a sponsor?
30. Why does April think she is ready?
31. Discuss the complexity of Rhonda's character. Were you surprised by her disclosure?
32. What do you think happens after the story ends? What new beginnings are possible?

Writers On The Edge offers a range of essays, memoirs and poetry written by major contemporary authors who bring fresh insight into the dark world of addiction, from drugs and alcohol, to sex, gambling and food. Editors Diana M. Raab and James Brown have assembled an array of talented and courageous writers who share their stories with heartbreaking honesty as they share their obsessions as well as the awe-inspiring power of hope and redemption.

"Open to any piece in this collection, and the scalding, unflinching, overwhelming truths within will shine light on places most people never look. Anyone who reads this book, be they users or used, will put it down changed. And when they raise their eyes from the very last page, the world they see may be redeemed, as well."

--Jerry Stahl, author of *Permanent Midnight*

"*Writers On The Edge* is a thoughtful compendium of first-person narratives by writers who have managed to use their despair to create beauty. A must-read for anyone in the recovery field."

--Leonard Buschel, Founder, Writers in Treatment

CONTRIBUTORS: Frederick & Steven Barthelme, Kera Bolonik, Margaret Bullitt-Jonas, Maud Casey, Anna David, Denise Duhamel, B.H. Fairchild, Ruth Fowler, David Huddle Perie Longo, Gregory Orr, Victoria Patterson, Molly Peacock, Scott Russell Sanders, Stephen Jay Schwartz, Linda Gray Sexton, Sue William Silverman, Chase Twichell, and Rachel Yoder

paperback * hardcover * eBook

ISBN 978-1-61599-108-2

From Modern History Press

CPSIA information can be obtained
at www.ICGtesting.com
Printed in the USA
BVHW041028231219
567573BV00022B/1075/P